To Sister Mary of the [illegible]
Happy birthday!
Love
Sissy

October 24, 1965

FAMOUS MODERN
MEN OF MEDICINE

by Caroline A. Chandler, M.D.

ILLUSTRATED WITH PHOTOGRAPHS

Dodd, Mead & Company · New York

920. 02

To
Jacqueline, Caroline and John F. Kennedy, Jr.
for whom
"what to come in yours and my discharge"
and
John Fitzgerald Kennedy
for whom
what's prologue is past

ACKNOWLEDGMENTS

The author is deeply indebted to many people for their generous help in the preparation of this manuscript. Special thanks are extended:

To those biographees I was able to interview—for their time and gracious patience. To those I was unable to see, through no fault of theirs—for gracing these pages anyway;

To professional colleagues: Dr. William G. Hollister, Dr. Jenny Waelder Hall, Dr. Sarah Tower, Dr. Anny Katan, Dr. Lois Murphy and Dr. Gardner Murphy—for consultation in special areas and wise counsel in general;

To professional co-workers in the National Institutes of Health: Dr. Charlotte Silverman, Mrs. Lura Jackson, Mr. Walter Clark, Mrs. Mildred Arrill—for providing expert assistance in the areas of public health, writing, art and photography, social science, and most especially to Mrs. Mary Gray—for researching and assisting in the preparation of pages 105–145.

To a few choice people who labored above and beyond the call of duty: Mrs. Naomi S. Peres, my secretary—for masterminding the entire production; Miss Elizabeth Howe, loyal fan since age ten, now a sophomore at author's alma mater, Barnard College, for acting as reader and reactor; Mrs. Mary Kerber—for voluntary typing assistance;

To "Little Doc" for seeing this through with his all;

Finally, to my mother, Lucile B. Chandler—for her rose-colored glasses and unshakeable faith.

PREFACE

The writer who accepts the task of writing about his contemporaries implicitly accepts the risk of losing friends and
alienating people. When, in addition, he agrees to take responsibility for selecting from among the entire roster of potential candidates not more than a dozen or so for inclusion
in a volume such as this, he does so at his own peril.

So by way of explanation, here are some of the criteria the
author developed in the course of making the hard choices
involved. It goes without saying the most clear-cut criterion
was that the biographees had to be both famous and of un-
questioned integrity and professional competence in the eyes
of their colleagues.

Another fairly obvious criterion was that coverage of the
various medical sciences should be broad enough to give some
notion of the revolutionary changes taking place in all areas
of medicine today. At the same time, it seemed equally important to single out for more extensive coverage in depth
those specialties most closely related to new scientific developments such as modern surgery and the surgical subspecialties, or those related to areas of high public interest
such as psychiatry and the various child-centered specialties.
This accounts for the obvious over-representation of surgery,
psychiatry and the child specialties at the expense of some of
the other medical sciences.

These then are some of the considerations which guided

the author in making choices that finally narrowed the field of potential candidates from several score to several dozen.

From this point on there are never any guidelines that can help in arriving at final decisions; final choices inevitably involve value judgments and, of necessity, these can only be the author's value judgments.

In the end, therefore, the author is left to account for his decisions in terms of his own value system. Since those who are called the "doers" in this book share in common qualities which characterize the "facilitators" included in the last chapter—and since the qualities highlighted in that chapter clearly reflect the author's point of view—it is hoped that the following quote from "What's Past Is Prologue" should serve this purpose.

"The examples cited above should give us a clue to the answer. They are all men of integrity, courage, vision, with a deep and abiding concern for their fellow men. But they are something more. They are men who have a unique kind of ability to convert theory and trial into tried and proven, to translate aspiration into action, to transform concept into concrete. They are also men who in their passion for justice will forever 'disturb the comfortable and comfort the disturbed.' They are above all men committed to a quality of excellence which makes them unable to give less than their best but, in the interim when choices must be weighed and decisions made, are able to 'tolerate uncertainty with equanimity.' "

Caroline A. Chandler, M.D.

CONTENTS

MARTHA MAY ELIOT

Pioneer in Public Health and in
Maternal and Child Health

[1891–   ]

"I<small>F I HAD</small> the chance, I would go anywhere any time to talk about what needs to be done, what needs to be changed—*there must be change.*" * This is still the battle cry of a person who, in a lifetime of public service, has brought about more change for the health and welfare of children than any other individual of our generation—valiant defender of the rights of *all* children, Dr. Martha Eliot.

Martha May Eliot, the daughter of (Reverend) Christopher Rhodes and Mary Jackson (May) Eliot, was born in Dorchester, Massachusetts, on April 7, 1891.

After graduation from public school at the age of thirteen, Martha was admitted to the fashionable Windsor School in Boston, in spite of the fact that she failed every question in arithmetic on the entrance examination! It was not until she was a grown woman, years later, that Martha discovered she had been Miss Windsor's "guest" during her five years at the Windsor School. Her "invitation" had been a confidential transaction between Miss Windsor and Martha's mother, who

Personal Interview with Dr. Eliot on June 28, 1964.

had been girlhood friends. It seems Miss Windsor's kind and generous act was prompted by her recognition of the fact that a poor, struggling, young Unitarian minister could never have afforded to send his daughter to a private school.

Miss Windsor's investment was a sound one, because it laid the educational foundation for Martha Eliot's brilliant academic and professional career. After receiving her A.B. degree from Radcliffe, she went on to the Johns Hopkins School of Medicine, graduating in 1918 with the degree of Doctor of Medicine. Years later, she was to win additional academic accolades in the form of honorary degrees—Sc.D., L.H.D. and LL.D.

In line with the adage quoted in the Preface, "What's past is prologue," and in the final summarizing of this book, it is not surprising that Martha Eliot chose a life of public service after years of specialized training in pediatrics. Her grandfather, William Greenleaf Eliot, emigrated from Massachusetts to St. Louis, Missouri, where, in 1834, he founded the first Unitarian church. In 1853, he established the Eliot Seminary. In 1857, this became the Washington University of St. Louis, of which he was the first president. A man dedicated to the principle that the "truth shall set men free," he established one of the first public schools in St. Louis, the "Mission Free School." He also inaugurated the first school of nursing at Washington University. He was an "abolitionist" during the Civil War.

When Reverend Christopher Eliot, the son of William Eliot, moved his family from Dorchester, Massachusetts, to the "West End" of Boston, he did so to take charge of a small Unitarian church, the "Bulfinch Place Church" on Beacon Hill. Everyone was welcome at the Bulfinch Place Church—the lame, the halt, the good, the bad, the white, the

14

black, the young, the old, the rich, the poor. But especially welcome were the working people who then inhabited the cobblestone streets of Beacon Hill, later to become famous and fashionable.

To accommodate his parishioners, who had to work on Sunday mornings, the Reverend Christopher held his services, not on Sunday morning, but in the afternoon and evening. Sunday evening was "Open House" at the church, where free coffee and doughnuts were dispensed to all comers.

Dr. Martha Eliot believes that all three Eliot children, her brother, her sister and herself, were profoundly influenced during their early years by their involvement in all the activities of the Bulfinch Place Church. Their whole family life centered around the church, which was as much a social center as a religious one. The children grew up with a sense of social responsibility so indelibly imprinted on each of them that it molded their careers. Martha's brother, Fredrick May Eliot, became a Unitarian minister. Following in the footsteps of his eminent grandfather, he left Massachusetts, headed west and settled in St. Paul, Minnesota. As minister of the Unity Church in that city, he spent over twenty years serving all comers, even as his father before him had done at Bulfinch Place. He died in 1958. Dr. Martha Eliot summed up his life's work in a single sentence, "He liked people."

The third Eliot child, Abigail Adams Eliot, is Martha's younger sister by one year. In her chosen field of nursery school education, Abigail Eliot has blazed a trail not unlike the one Martha Eliot has blazed in the field of child health and welfare. Today, although officially "retired," Dr. Abigail Eliot is a very "unretired" consultant to the nursery school teacher training program she was instrumental in developing. The Eliot-Pearson Teacher Training School at Tufts University, in Boston, is one of the few fully accredited college level departments for training nursery school teachers in the entire United States. So grew another seedling from the mighty Bulfinch Place tree!

After graduation from medical school, Martha Eliot began her lengthy training in pediatrics as a house officer at the Peter Bent Brigham Hospital in Boston. From there she went next to the St. Louis Children's Hospital, came back to the Massachusetts General Hospital in Boston, then went on to the New Haven Hospital, where she finished her residency. She was appointed to the pediatric teaching staff of the Yale School of Medicine in 1921 and by 1932 had risen to the rank of associate clinical professor.

Martha Eliot's public life officially began when she was appointed Director of the Division of Maternal and Child Health of the United States Children's Bureau in 1924.

At that time, the Children's Bureau was administratively under the United States Department of Labor. This was no freak accident of governmental bureaucracy. There was every reason why the Children's Bureau should have been launched under the aegis of the Department of Commerce and Labor in 1912 and a year later transferred to the newly created Department of Labor. Those were the days when stalwarts like Lillian Wald, founder of New York's Henry Street Settlement, and Florence Kelley of the National Consumer's League were spearheading the battle against child labor. Lillian Wald was the first person to advocate a Federal Children's Bureau when she coined her classic remark: "If the government can have a department to look after the Nation's farm crops, why can't it have a bureau to look after the Nation's child crop?" *

*Five decades of Action for Children. *Children's Bureau Publication No. 358, 1962 Revision, page 1.*

16

Dr. Eliot's service in the Children's Bureau covered a span of thirty-two years, from 1924 to 1956, when she retired as the fourth Chief of the Bureau. She served under two Bureau Chiefs, Miss Grace Abbott (1921–1933), and Miss Katherine F. Lenroot (1934–1951), before she herself succeeded to the top Bureau post. She was well prepared to take over the reins when President Truman appointed her Bureau Chief in 1951. From her starting position as a division chief in 1924, she rose to become Assistant Chief of the Bureau in 1934 and Associate Chief in 1941. During those years she lived through the "hard times" of the early twenties, the great depression years of the thirties, the war-torn years of the forties and the postwar adjustments of the early fifties! During those decades, the gallant women who led the Children's Bureau took on the long, hard, lonely, and often unpopular job of fighting for the rights of children.

It would be neither possible nor appropriate to list even the major accomplishments of the Children's Bureau in a biographical account of only one of its famous Chiefs. It would, however, be unfair to both subject and reader not to mention two pieces of legislation for children that were enacted by Congress during Martha Eliot's tenure and which she was active in developing and implementing. One was the long-term and now well-established Children's Section of the Social Security Act; the other was a short-term measure, known as EMIC, designed to meet an emergency situation during World War II.

The major provisions of the so-called "Children's Titles" of the Social Security Act are contained in the following paragraph:

During the years 1934–40, the Bureau concentrated on building the maternal and child health, crippled children, and child welfare programs under the Social Security Act of 1935, first helping to mold the Act and then planning for and initiating the administration of these three programs as provided for in its Title V. *

The other measure approved and passed by Congress during the war was EMIC, or the Emergency Maternal and Infant Care program. This was "the largest public maternity program ever undertaken in the United States. It provided wives of aviation cadets and of servicemen in the fourth to seventh grades of all the services, free medical, nursing and hospital care throughout pregnancy, at childbirth and for six weeks thereafter. It also provided for medical, nursing and hospital care for the babies of these servicemen during their first year." †

Although Katherine Lenroot was Chief of the Children's Bureau during the time Congress enacted these two historic milestones in legislation for children, and is rightly given major credit for their success, without Martha Eliot's quiet foot-slogging, Congressional action might have been delayed or, in the case of EMIC, failed altogether. For it fell to Dr. Eliot, as the Bureau's top-ranking physician, to take on the job of interpreting and "selling" the health and medical sections of social welfare bills not only to the Congress but also to the medical profession. Anyone familiar with the record of legislation in the health field could never accuse the Congressional "Establishment" of being "soft" on tax-supported medical care programs. Consequently, Dr. Eliot, in testifying for the EMIC bill during hearings held by committees of both the House and the Senate, had to participate in that exhaustive question-and-answer ritual which has become an

*"A Half Century of Progress for All Children." Reprinted by the U.S. Department of Health, Education, and Welfare, Social Security Administration Children's Bureau from Children, March–April 1962, page 45.
†Ibid., page 46.

integral and necessary part of the hearing process. But throughout the entire proceedings, she was treated by the gentlemen of the Congress with the dignity and respect they invariably accord trusted and valued members of government agencies.

This, unfortunately, was not the case when she participated in "hearings" held by some of her confreres of the medical "Establishment." These "gentlemen" not only attacked the bill itself, instantly and automatically damning it as "socialized medicine," they also challenged the honor and integrity of its defender. Although the bill ultimately was passed and Martha Eliot went through her ordeal by fire with courage, dignity and grace, one can only guess at what cost, for the battle scars left by searing engagements like these are never glorified by battle stripes, since they leave no marks on the body, only on the soul.

After her retirement from the Children's Bureau in 1956, Dr. Eliot began her second career by accepting the post of Professor and Head of the Department of Maternal and Child Health at the Harvard School of Public Health, a position she held until she reached the age of mandatory retirement in 1960.

Today, Dr. Eliot is well into the fifth year of her *third* career as Chairman of the Massachusetts Commission on Children and Youth! And although, in the genteel jargonese of old-line New England social agencies, she is technically a "citizen volunteer," Martha Eliot is working full time with all the zest and energy she has poured into every other "voluntary" assignment she has performed with distinction. These include her posts as Assistant Director-General of WHO (Geneva 1949–51); Vice-chairman U.S., Delegate to the International Health Conference (1946); Chief Medical Consultant U.N., to the International Children's Emergency Fund (1947); U.S. Representative on the Executive Board of the United Nations Children's Fund (1952–57); and Chairman of the Expert Committee on Maternal and Child Health of the World Health Organization (1949).

The task that Dr. Martha Eliot has set herself to accomplish for children in her present role is a staggering one, and for anyone else, an impossible one. As Chairman of the MCCY, she is heading up a project designed to bring health and mental health services to all children and families in the state of Massachusetts who need them and are not getting them. This project was undertaken by the Commission at the request of the Health and Welfare Council, with the backing of official state agencies and the many old-line family agencies which have been the pride of the Bay State since its early beginnings. And such is the esteem and trust in which Martha Eliot is held, that the Commission she heads was selected to carry out a project which almost inevitably will entail changes in long-established agency practices, including the right of sovereign domain over separate but overlapping services.

Toward the end of my visit with Dr. Eliot, she talked at length about her new venture. When she got into the realm of ideas, expectations and hopes, I was suddenly struck with the strange feeling that I knew what she was going to say next— that somehow I had heard, read or conjured up a dream identical to the one she was projecting. It wasn't until I arrived back home that I remembered in a flash where I had both heard and read all this before. I checked my files and there it was—the blueprint for Martha Eliot's present dream as she had drawn it some ten years ago. It seems appropriate to conclude with that version of a dream which was first dreamed around the turn of the century on Bulfinch Place.

Too many of our public and private agencies, our health, social welfare, and education programs, our churches and youth-serving organizations have worked in isolation from each other with courtesy nods, only, between them. . . . By this very separateness, I am convinced we are either wasting, or not using, tremendous social energy. We are failing to reach countless children who could use some help. By building emotional, as well as brick walls around our individual institutions and agencies, we are limiting our capacity to help. . . .

To be as bold and inventive as the atomic scientists, calls for sharpening our perception of children's needs. Even more, it calls for courage: the courage to face reality, to reconize the implications of what we are doing or failing to do; the courage to invent, to experiment, and to test new ways of working together.*

*Eliot, Martha M.: "Putting Social Fission and Fusion to Work for Children." Speech to the National Council of Churches of Christ in America, Cleveland, Ohio, November 1955.

HOWARD A. RUSK

Pioneer in Rehabilitation

[1901–   ]

Sick people throughout the world ask their God, "Why must I suffer?" Possibly the answer comes in the word of the potter. Great ceramics are not made by putting clay in the sun; they come only from the white heat of the kiln. In the firing process, some pieces are broken but those that survive the heat are transformed from clay into objects of art, and so it is, it seems to me, with sick, suffering and crippled people. Those who, through medical skill, opportunity, work and courage, survive their illness or overcome their handicap and take their places back in the world have a depth of spirit that you and I can hardly measure. They haven't wasted their pain.*

*T*HE AUTHOR of the excerpt quoted is Director of the Institute of Physical Medicine and Rehabilitation of the New York University Medical Center and Chairman of the Department of Physical Medicine and Rehabilitation, New York University School of Medicine. He is also the former wartime Chief of Convalescent Services, United States Air Forces, and the present president of the World Rehabilitation Fund, Inc. He is, in addition, the possessor of half a dozen honorary

From an interview with Edward R. Murrow over radio station WCBS. Reprinted from Help, Inc., 1953.

degrees and the recipient of awards ranging from the Lasker
Award of the American Public Health Association to that of
Chevalier, French Legion of Honor.

One of the most intriguing problems the average person
faces in sizing up a public figure is trying to reconcile what
a man says with what he is. The relationship of the two paragraphs above is a case in point. How can an internationally
renowned giant of the stature of Dr. Howard A. Rusk, pre-
sumably far removed from the everyday cares and anxieties
of the ordinary man, be so deeply understanding and exqui-
sitely sensitive to the pain of the ordinary man?

The answer is, of course, that Howard Rusk started out in
life as an ordinary human being himself and there is every
reason to believe he underwent his fair share of human suffering, including personal pain. One early incident, related by
Orin Lehman,* is particularly significant because it must have
left a deep scar on the soul of a sensitive, teen-age boy.

For two summers during his four years at Brookfield (Missouri) High School, "Rusty" Rusk went off to St. Louis to
attend summer school. It so happens that one of those summers
he arrived in St. Louis with a nasal disorder that ultimately
led to minor surgery. Unfortunately, the physician to whom
he was referred by the school not only callously ridiculed the
boy's discomfort but was actually sadistic to the point of
performing the surgery without giving him anesthesia of any
kind. This cruel and humiliating experience made a deep and
lasting impression on a boy whose "most characteristic fea-
ture," according to one of his professors, was "his desire to
help other folks."

After graduation from Brookfield High School, "Rusty"

*Lehman, Orin: "The Early Life of Howard A. Rusk, M.D., 1901–1945,"
Thesis, June, 1961.

23

began his college career at the University of Missouri, in Columbia. His college years were highlighted by two events, one happy and one unhappy, that became landmarks in his development. The happy one came during his freshman year. It was his meeting with Wesley McAfee, who became his best and lifelong friend. The unhappy event occurred in his junior year, when his father, Michael Yost Rusk, lost all his money. From that time on, Howard Rusk worked his way through the rest of college and all the way through medical school, first at the University of Missouri and later as a transfer to the University of Pennsylvania School of Medicine. As he himself puts it, "I worked as a hospital orderly, I washed test tubes for laboratories at night, I took on any job I could find to pay my way through medical school." *

When he finished medical school in 1925, Howard Rusk went back to St. Louis, where, following his hospital residency training, he settled down to the practice of internal medicine. A year later, he married Gladys Houx of Marshall, Missouri. She had been a college classmate at the University of Missouri. Between the time of his marriage in 1926 up to the outbreak of World War II, in 1941, Howard Rusk managed to build up a $60,000 a year practice, with some 4000 patients on his roster, acquire a beautiful home and become the father of three children—Martha Rusk (Sutphen), Howard A. Rusk, Jr., and John Michael Rusk.

In 1942, Dr. Rusk was commissioned as a major in the U.S. Army Air Force and assigned to Jefferson Barracks, Missouri, as the medical officer in charge of a convalescent ward. It was here that the boy whose burning desire had been to "help other folks" finally came into his own. The vague, restless discontent he had felt during his years of practice as one of

*Personal interview with the author, July 1964.

"the finest internists in St. Louis" vanished when he was faced with seriously ill patients, rather than with the minor maladies and neuroses that are the bread and butter fare of the popular practitioner.

From his experience both as a lowly hospital orderly and as a medical resident, Rusk had come to the conclusion that "hospitalization is 10 per cent pain and 90 per cent boredom." So at Jefferson Barracks he devised a treatment program for ward patients that combined physical exercise with military education. Curricula were developed and courses were set up to teach everything from the intricacies of radio transmission to the simple mechanics of ordinary lifesaving techniques. The motto of the day became, "While you are sick in a hospital today, you may learn something that will save your life six months from now."

It was also at Jefferson Barracks that Howard Rusk carried out his first controlled experiment in rehabilitation. Using a time-honored research technique, he divided a ward of 600 men who had virus pneumonia into two groups. One group (A) was given medical treatment alone; the other group (B), in addition to receiving the same medical treatment, was given the "works" in terms of exercise, education and motivation. And the result? Group A patients stayed in the hospital an average of forty-five days as compared with Group B, whose average stay was thirty-one days. Even more striking, however, was the difference in the rate of relapse, or recurrence of virus pneumonia, between the two groups. The recurrence rate in Group A was 30 per cent; in Group B it was 3 per cent!

Word of this successful experiment at Jefferson Barracks "shot with bullet-like speed to the Pentagon brass." * The

*Lehman, Orin: "The Early Life of Howard A. Rusk, M.D., 1901–1945."

replying salvo from the "brass" was equally speedy. On orders of the Commanding General of the American Air Forces, General H. H. Arnold, Dr. Rusk was transferred forthwith to Washington, with the "request" that he initiate and develop a broad-scale convalescent program for the A.A.F. Beginning in March 1943, Rusk served as Chief of the Convalescent Training Division in the Office of the Air Surgeon until his discharge as a full colonel in the fall of 1945. During that period, he organized and set in motion a convalescent program that encompassed 253 hospitals and 12 special Rehabilitation Centers. In this program, every conceivable type of training was offered in the way of music, art, and drama, as well as specialized training for highly skilled jobs. As for treatment services, the "smorgasbord" available ranged from medicine and surgery to psychotherapy and resocialization. The cardinal principles of rehabilitative treatment as developed by Dr. Rusk and Dr. Taylor, a colleague and fellow officer who had become Rusk's "strong right arm," were described in a scientific journal in May 1945 as follows:

1. Treat the whole man regardless of what his needs may be.
2. Treat the patient as an individual.
3. Give early, continuous and progressive therapy from the earliest possible moment following acute illness or injury until maximum possible benefits have been received.*

Two other books on rehabilitation that have become "Bibles" in this field are A.A.F. Manual No. 23, *Handbook to Recovery*, put out by the A.A.F. Training Aids Division in 1944, and *New Hope for the Handicapped* by Dr. Rusk and Dr. Taylor, published by Harper in 1946.

*Rusk, H. A., and Taylor, E. J.: "Army Air Forces Convalescent Training Program," Annals of the American Academy of Political and Social Sciences, CCXXXIX, 53, May 1945.

After the war, Howard Rusk returned to St. Louis to try his hand at the practice of medicine again, but his heart wasn't in it. His experience in the A.A.F. had sparked a fire in him to "teach and practice rehabilitation," which now seemed unquenchable. When Washington University in St. Louis was not ready to establish a rehabilitation department, Rusk turned his practice over to his two assistants, sold his house, and moved his family and belongings, lock, stock, and barrel, to New York City.

Fortunately for him, in the course of serving on committees, Dr. Rusk had met Arthur Hays Sulzberger, publisher of the *New York Times*. Sulzberger was a member of the Central Committee of the American Red Cross. His interest in rehabilitation equaled Rusk's, and he had tried to get the A.R.C. to set up a rehabilitation program after the war, but the A.R.C. Board had vetoed his proposal on the grounds that it would be too costly.

When Rusk arrived in New York City, he went to see Sulzberger, in order to obtain the publisher's help in interesting one of the New York universities in a rehabilitation program. Sulzberger replied by offering the doctor a job on his newspaper, with the statement that "the New York Times is the greatest university in the world." At first Rusk turned down the offer on the grounds that he was "a doctor, not a writer." But Sulzberger persisted, and on December 8, 1945, Rusk capitulated. What finally proved to be irresistible to the latter were the terms of the offer Sulzberger made. Rusk relates the following conversation: *Rusk* "What shall I write?" *Sulzberger*—"Write what you believe in." *Rusk*—"When?" *Sulzberger*—"Whenever convenient." *Rusk*—"How much space?" *Sulzberger*—"Whatever you want."

Howard Rusk's first article, entitled "Rehabilitation," appeared in the *New York Times* on December 9, 1945. With that article the die was cast and the dedicated doctor knew that, from then on, for him there could be no turning back. His life's work would be writing, teaching, doing, living and breathing rehabilitation.

Today Howard Rusk is living out his multifaceted dream. As Associate Editor of the *New York Times*, he continues to educate the public on rehabilitation by writing his own newspaper column, which appears in the *Times*. He has written several more books and has contributed a number of articles to medical journals. He has been written about in magazines such as *Look, Time*, and *McCall's* and has been the subject of TV and radio presentations running the gamut from interview to documentary.

Teaching, training and doing rehabilitation are part of his everyday life at the Institute of Physical Medicine and Rehabilitation (IPMR), a unit of the New York University College of Medicine. This magnificent structure overlooking New York's East River was opened in 1951. It is the tangible result of Howard Rusk's years of dreaming, planning and back-breaking fund raising.

I interviewed Dr. Rusk in his office on the sixth floor of the Institute.* Sitting at his imposing desk, the wall behind him covered with plaques, statuettes and other insignia of innumerable awards, Howard Rusk could be mistaken for an industrial tycoon. He is a big, handsome man, and it is not until he begins to speak—with his eyes, his hands and his voice—that you recognize in a flash the man who was the boy whose one desire was "to help other folks."

In answer to my first question, he told me that the Institute is now training some sixty doctors a year from the United

Personal interview with the author, July 1964.

States and from countries all over the world in what he calls "the third phase of medicine." He distinguishes the "third phase" from the "first" (preventive) and the "second" (treatment) by describing it as the "phase which *helps the patient from bed to job and community*." This is done by meeting the "total needs of the patient—physical, emotional, spiritual and vocational."

About half of the 141 beds in the Institute (106 for adults, 35 for children), are subsidized and there are few private rooms. Patients come from around the globe, and all are treated in terms of their disabilities, not in terms of their bank accounts.

I asked about the range of disabilities being treated at the Institute and Dr. Rusk replied, "Everything from stroke patients to paraplegics and broken necks. . . . The children's unit has mentally retarded children and kids with cerebral palsy and various congenital defects."

Then I asked about some of the results of treatment. "After an average of seven weeks of training, 35 per cent of stroke patients are back at work," he told me. "For those with broken necks who make it back to college or job, the average training time is 180 days."

My final question was, "What is the magic ingredient of the 'third phase of medicine'? Is it the patient's will to get well? Is it the specialized training he gets here? Or, is it the extraordinary skill of your talented staff?"

He answered, "It's a little of everything you've mentioned, but it is something else too. You see, you and I only use about 25 per cent of our capacity—a blind man uses 100 per cent of his! Here we train people to use *all their unused capacity in place of what they have lost.* It's really very simple. That's why I keep saying 85 per cent of the handicapped can be trained to work and that no handicapped person is too handicapped to work."

As I left, Dr. Rusk obligingly answered my plea for some written biographical material by loaning me his own copy of the Orin Lehman thesis (the only bound copy in existence!), together with sheafs of reprints.

Among the latter was a reprint of *This I Believe*, from which the paragraph quoted at the beginning of this sketch was taken. I can think of no better way to end this brief picture of Howard Rusk than to quote verbatim the final paragraphs of *This I Believe*: *

Because of this experience (suffering), they have a desire to share that is almost a compulsion. It matters not whether they be a physician from India, a Zionist from Israel, a Greek veteran or a Pole disabled in a mining accident—all want to share the understanding they have gained through suffering or by helping those who have suffered.

I believe that this basic and inherent desire of man to do something for his less fortunate fellow transcends religious dogmas, political beliefs and geographical barriers. If we could only use this universal language, we would have a tool to unravel the babel of tongues and an instrument which would penetrate any iron curtain or closed boundary.

It does not seem strange to me that the sick should turn to those who have suffered for their greatest comfort. And so, in a sick world, it is not strange that we turn to those who have been ravaged by suffering and disease for a common language. If we could start to work here together in a program where all of us have the same goals, it is more than possible that, with God's help, we would find the solution for living together in peace. This I believe!

See footnote 1, page 22.

THE MEN OF MENNINGER

Pioneers in the Development of a Community Mental Health Program

[1862–   ]

A FAMOUS colleague and close friend of Dr. "Karl" and Dr. "Will" Menninger once described the Menninger Clinic as "a unique institution that only the American Midwest could have spawned, being at one and the same time as indigenous as the prairies of Kansas and as cosmopolitan as the couches of Park Avenue!"

The Menninger Foundation of today is "a nonprofit organization for psychiatric treatment, training, and research, and for the prevention of mental illness. It is the outgrowth of the Menninger Clinic, founded in 1919 by Dr. C. F. Menninger and his sons, Dr. Karl A. and Dr. William C. Menninger. The clinic operated a private psychiatric hospital, a school for problem children, and a small research and training program. In 1946, the Menningers turned their assets over to the Menninger Foundation. The Foundation helps give psychiatric training in the Topeka Veterans Administration hospital and other Kansas hospitals. It also conducts research, and operates a department for children, an industrial mental-health program, and a marriage-counseling training program.

The Foundation is located at 3617 West 6th Street, Topeka, Kansas." *

In all the write-ups of the famous Menninger Clinic in Topeka, one of the features seldom if ever mentioned is its setting. It is an incredible experience, in this day and age, to visit one of the most *avant garde*, community psychiatric clinics in the United States, only to discover that it resembles more than anything else a sprawling, magnificent ante-bellum estate! The various buildings which house the four major departments of the Foundation—professional education, research, social psychiatry and the Menninger Clinic itself— cover an area of about six hundred acres and spread from the east side of Topeka to the west. Many of the buildings, except for the spanking new Rosenberry Activities Therapy Building and the new children's unit, are remodeled editions of the lovely old frame houses in which the various members of the Menninger clan grew up. Even the refurbishing the houses have undergone in order to accommodate the demands of modern living has not in any way dimmed their luster as gracious period pieces of an earlier America when people in towns built residences that were not "town houses" but homes.

The preceding descriptive paragraph is given more space than it may seem to warrant for a specific purpose—it is an attempt to capture in words the indigenous flavor of the Menninger style, which is "family style." Physically, the family touch is everywhere evident—from the trees, all tagged with their botanical names by Dr. C. F. M., to the Historical Museum, which is the repository of an incredible array of Menninger treasures and trophies, ranging from shell collec-

---

Menninger, William C.: World Book Encyclopedia, *Field Enterprises Educational Corporation, Vol. 12, p. 326, 1960.*

tions and early American Indian art to historic family papers and documents.

The family touch, psychologically, is also all-pervasive, but it is of a different order altogether. This becomes clear only when the visitor on a conducted tour through the Clinic finally comes face to face with the Menninger brothers themselves and finds, much to his surprise, two warm, human beings, instead of the famous,* awesomely honored clinic cornerstones he was prepared to meet.

Dr. Karl, whose title is Chief of Staff, is a tall, striking man of distinction—academic style. Even in the brief time I spent with him I began to get a glimmer of why the man who wrote such books as *The Human Mind* (1930), *Man Against Himself* (1938), *Love Against Hate* (1942), and *A Manual for Psychiatric Case Study* (1952; rev. ed., 1962) should be the same man who, in an obituary for a friend, wrote: "This was Dave whom we loved—our friend, the friend of all people, a great and noble man, a gentle man. We shall not look upon his like again. But he is here; he lives in us, and his life is all around us. His voice is in the voice you have just heard; and if you listen, you will hear his heart beat; it is your own." †

Karl Menninger is a sensitive, understanding physician, a scholarly professor of psychiatry, an impulsive crusader and a pixie-like stormy petrel—all rolled into one. Being with him gives one the sensation of plunging headlong through the looking glass and, as Alice discovered, it is an exhilarating, heady, breathtaking, unbelievable but altogether wonderful experience! It is one I will never forget.

The reader is referred to Who's Who in America, *Vol. 33; 1963–1964, for a complete list of the honorary degrees, awards and other honors that have been conferred on Dr. Karl Augustus Menninger and Dr. William Claire Menninger.*

†The Menninger Foundation Report of Progress, *1962–1963, p. 8.*

The rest of the story of the Menninger Clinic is based on a lengthy session I had with Dr. Will. It seemed quite natural to choose him as the principal person to ask to interview when I visited the Clinic because he is the only member of the clan I had met before. Also, to be perfectly frank, I was glad to have a legitimate reason for requesting an interview because, from the moment I first met Will Menninger, I knew if I ever wrote a sequel to my first book about medical "greats," * he would be in it. What follows, therefore, is an example of a sort of self-fulfilling prophecy.

William Claire Menninger is one of the three sons of Dr. Charles Frederick and Flora Knisely Menninger. He, like his brother Karl before him, went to Washburn College, in Topeka, as an undergraduate. Unlike Karl, however, who went to Harvard for his medical training, Will chose to study medicine at Cornell, where he received his M.D. degree in 1924. Before he settled down in Topeka to become a full-fledged partner in the family enterprise, he served an eighteen-month internship in medicine and surgery at New York's Bellevue Hospital. Sometime later, he returned to the East long enough to take postgraduate training in psychiatry at St. Elizabeth's Hospital, Washington, D.C.

Although he is now president of the Menninger Foundation and professor of psychiatry in the Menninger School of Psychiatry, Dr. Will spends one half of his time away from Topeka, campaigning for the mental health movement. In this role, which he took on reluctantly and which he regards as necessary, but too close to Madison Avenue for comfort, he makes speeches before lay groups, gives lectures to professional groups and delivers impassioned addresses to State legisla-

*Chandler, Caroline A.: Famous Men of Medicine, Dodd, Mead & Co., 1950.

tures—all in an effort to educate, raise funds and advance the cause of mental health in general. Anyone who has ever heard Will Menninger address a formal assembly of State legislators, and watched him move seasoned oratorical pros to tears and cheers would have to say that he, although a reluctant dragon, puts on a brilliant performance! *

No one really knows how many dollars have been raised for State and local mental health programs as a result of Will Menninger's barnstorming, but it is safe to estimate that the figure could be reckoned not in thousands, but in millions of dollars by now. What *is* known however, is that in every State where Will Menninger has spoken before State legislatures, the appropriation for the State's mental health program has been upped.

In writing to thank Dr. Will for sending me a reprint of an article he wrote for the Boy Scout magazine, *Boys' Life,*† called "Medicine, My Way of Life," I said: "Your style of writing is wonderfully free and easy, or, as my secretary puts it, 'it's as if he were sitting in the opposite chair from you and having a friendly chat.' " I can think of no better way to describe the man behind the style with whom I did have a friendly chat than in much the same words. He *is* free and easy. He is also big and brotherly, genial and gentle. And he is, above all, a "caretaker" in the best sense of the word because he takes care *of* people by caring *for* them.

We began our chat with statistics and ended it with hobbies and philosophies. I learned, for example, that since the Foundation first began training psychiatrists in 1931, nearly 800

*At the invitation of Governor Millard Tawes, Dr. William C. Menninger addressed a special session of the Joint Assembly of the Maryland State Legislature on February 8, 1962. His appearance was sponsored by The Maryland Association for Mental Health. The author attended the session as a member of the Board of the MAMH.

†Boys' Life, March 1964.

physicians have had all or part of their training in the Menninger School of Psychiatry. These physicians have come from all areas of the United States and many other countries. For example, the thirty physicians who entered the three-year psychiatric training program in July 1963 came from twelve States and Argentina, Australia, Canada, Cuba, Greece, Hungary, Mexico and Spain. The three-year program for doctors includes training at the Topeka Veterans Administration Hospital, the Topeka State Hospital, the Menninger Foundation, and the other Kansas State hospitals.

In addition to training physicians who ultimately will become adult or child psychiatrists, the Foundation also provides fully accredited, postgraduate training for psychologists and social workers. The program in "adjunctive therapy" includes training in occupational therapy, music therapy and recreational therapy. Last—but by no means least—there is a one-year doctoral program in theology and psychiatric theory for graduate theologians and a training course in pastoral care and counseling for clergymen. Surely the Menninger Foundation is doing its part to alleviate the acute shortages of manpower in the mental health field!

I had been told that Dr. Will collects stamps, so I asked him about this hobby and hobbies in general. He calls his stamp collecting "a refueling operation" and explains that he gets "enormous satisfaction from finding a ten-cent stamp after looking for it for three years." About stamps he said, "They don't have to be persuaded—you don't have to argue with them. If you make mistakes with them, they're your *own* mistakes!"

As for hobbies in general, he is strongly in favor of them and recommends them to his patients. He feels that family hobbies or "family projects" are vitally important because they are "creative" and because "they get a family to build together, to plan together, to work together." He makes it perfectly clear that he sees a family project or hobby not as an end in itself, but as a means to an end when he asks, "How, in heavens name, can you teach people to get along with each other if you haven't learned how to get along with your own family?"

He counts as his greatest personal blessing the fact that his three sons—Roy Wright, Philip Bratton and William Walter Menninger—have now come back to Topeka to become "co-builders" in the family Foundation.

When we got around to discussing Dr. Will's professional life, I asked, "Of all the things you have done, what gives you the most satisfaction now?" He replied, "The progress we've made in mental health" and . . . "here in Kansas we've lit a little candle." He then went on to tell me about some of the views he holds about life in general and the values he cherishes with deep conviction.

It is completely in character for Dr. Will to have become so concerned with the job I faced in trying to write this book that he offered everything short of doing it for me. When he sent me the reprint of his article from *Boys' Life,* I skimmed through it, thought how it sounded just like him, checked it against my notes and then sat down to write this account of the Menninger Clinic. Not until I was almost finished did it finally dawn on me that Dr. Will had written the end of this biography for me, handed it to me on a platter, and all I had to do was to use it!

So, with profound thanks to Dr. Will, I share with my readers some of the things he told me in his own words:

"I'm a doctor. My lifework is medicine. There are many sad and tedious parts of it. But for me, there has been great exhilaration and satisfaction in seeing sick people responding to treatment, from the feeling that I've had a little share in making life better for people who are in trouble. I've never felt that psychiatry, which is my specialty, can save the world all by itself. It presents no patent pill for ending war or meeting the threat of the atomic bomb—or even for getting children to stop biting their nails. Psychiatry, however, does help one to understand himself better and it helps us to understand other people.

"I believe the world can be a better place to live in if people are healthier in their minds. In dealing with emotional and mental illness, so much of the treatment process is concerned with the re-education of people and how they live their lives. In a sense, it is often a chance to teach them how to live more effectively, by understanding their own problems the better. I like to compare psychiatric treatment to a situation in which a person is stumbling around in a dark room, bumping up against the furniture, hurting himself and perhaps damaging the furniture. If a light can be turned on so that the person can see what he is bumping into, he is enabled to choose a more satisfactory path. He can then avoid the bumps and the hurting."

Dr. Will lists as yardsticks for measuring maturity the ability to "face reality, to adapt to change, to control anxieties, to give of yourself, to be considerate and to learn to love." In answer to the question "what is maturity?" here is his definition:

"It is the capacity to form personal relationships, to make and keep friends. One must learn from his mistakes. Don't always accept things as they are. Instead, if you feel something is wrong, step up and speak out against it. There are many things I don't want to accept and I am going to give my lifeblood, if necessary, to change them."

And finally:

"Whatever career you elect, however, never stop growing. My brothers and I were reared in a family atmosphere that emphasized learning. Our father urged us to study science, history and poetry. Our mother made us familiar with literature and religion. We were taught to be curious about everything. That was our great heritage, I think—curiosity. Throughout life, if I've learned any one thing, it has been that it's not all in the books, that I still have a lot to learn. Life—whatever your job—is a continuous, growing process."

THE MEN OF MAYO

Pioneers in the Group Practice of Medicine

[1864–   ]

As a tribute to William Worrall Mayo, the founding father of the Mayo Clinic, on September 12, 1964, the United States Post Office Department issued a commemorative stamp on the one hundredth anniversary of the date when he began the practice of medicine in Rochester, Minnesota, in 1864. The hundred and twenty million stamps making up the commemorative issue bear the sculptured likenesses of Dr. "Will" and Dr. "Charlie" Mayo as they were cast in bronze from a model designed by James Earl Fraser. The bronze statue itself towers majestically before the entrance to the present Clinic building, a ten-story, marble and aluminum product of the jet age. This building is one of the six that now constitute the complex called the "Mayo Clinic," covering an area of four city blocks and employing three thousand of Rochester's forty thousand inhabitants. The Clinic's automated records operation is such that it can process forty thousand histories, laboratory reports, X-ray readings, appointment cards, and discharge slips in a single day.

This example of putting the products of technology to use in the service of the lame and the halt is symbolic of the giant strides medicine has taken during a century of progress

—a century in which three generations of physicians named Mayo have played historic roles.

William Worrall Mayo, the third child and second son of James and Ann (Bonselle) Mayo, was born on May 31, 1819, in the village of Eccles, a hamlet located on the outskirts of Manchester, England. His father was a sea captain who, until his untimely death, plied his trade by sailing the seven seas. William was only seven when his father died and, by that time, one of the six children of his widowed mother. In spite of the difficulties a mother faces in raising six children alone, Mrs. Mayo managed to see that William got a good education, which included attending Owens College in Manchester. It was at Owens College that he studied under the famous chemist, John Dalton, whose impact on him was such that he was interested in chemistry throughout his life.

In 1845, at the age of twenty-six, William Mayo struck out for America. He arrived in New York and began his professional career in America by taking a job as a chemist in the drug department of Bellevue Hospital.

His sojourn in New York was brief because those were the days when frontier fever was running high and young men with blood in their veins were moving west. So young Mayo began a westward trek that took him first to Lafayette, Indiana, where he stayed for two years, studying medicine as an apprentice to Dr. Eleazar Deming. His next stop was St. Louis, where he completed his medical education and took his M.D., at the University of Missouri. After a brief backtrack to Lafayette, Indiana, where he taught anatomy in the medical school, he pushed on, first to St. Paul, and then to Le Sueur, Minnesota. During the Civil War he was provost surgeon for southern Minnesota, in charge of recruiting stations.

In 1863, Dr. Mayo moved to Rochester, Minnesota, and built his home on the corner of First Avenue and Second Street, Southwest, the site of the present Mayo Clinic. There he settled down with his wife, Louise Abigail Wright Mayo, and, a short time later, hung out a shingle which was destined to become the hallmark of a medical dynasty.

William James Mayo, the first son, had been born in Le Sueur, Minnesota, on July 29, 1861, toward the end of the westward trek. Charles Horace Mayo, his younger brother, was actually born in Rochester, on July 19, 1865. The two Mayo sons and the three Mayo daughters received their early education in the Rochester public schools. But the boys, in addition, became apprentices in medicine to their father. They assisted him after school hours and during summer vacations, in his office and on country house calls, so that by the time they finished high school, they were already well versed in the art of medicine and skilled assistants in surgical practice.

Up to the time when the brothers entered medical school, their paths were almost identical, but at the point of entry into formal training, they took divergent roads. William James went to the University of Michigan, in Ann Arbor, where, after taking the three-year course in medicine, he graduated in 1883. Charles Horace elected to attend the Chicago Medical College, then affiliated with Northwestern University. He entered medical school in 1885 and graduated in 1888.

By the time William James Mayo returned to Rochester to assist his father, the elder Dr. Mayo had become the leading physician not only of Rochester and Olmstead County but of the State itself and the surrounding territory. As news of his skill spread, patients from the Dakotas and Iowa began to appear on his doorstep and, since grateful patients attract other patients, they came in ever-increasing numbers and from a wider and wider radius. As a result, a father's starry-eyed dream of being able to enjoy a leisurely practice when his sons returned to assist him slowly dwindled in the face of reality. It vanished altogether only when it became clear that it would take many hard working pairs of extra hands to carry the mounting load of sick and disabled streaming into Rochester, seeking help. This was years before the Mayo establishment was first called a "medical mecca," but the handwriting was already on the wall for those who had eyes to see.

The transformation of a small family enterprise into an internationally renowned medical center began when Charles Horace Mayo came back from medical school to join his father and older brother in what is now called the group practice of medicine.

What are the landmarks that, above all others, stand out as decisive ones in the making of the "modern mecca" built by the hands of Mayo?

The first one, ironically enough, was built on a disaster. On August 21, 1883, a cyclone hit the northern section of Rochester with such force that some twenty people were killed and about twice that number were injured. Since the town had no hospital, Rommel's Dance Hall and some nearby lodge rooms of the German Library Association were converted into a temporary hospital and the injured were moved in. Dr. William Worrall Mayo was appointed by the City Council to take charge of the hospital operation and was given responsibility for procuring medical and nursing service, as well as supplies. Medical assistance and supplies were no problem because Dr. Mayo put his sons to work, along with several local physicians, and stocked the improvised hospital

43

with supplies from his own office. Finding nurses was a different story. Untrained lady volunteers were not lacking, but none of them could leave their families around the clock and the severely injured needed twenty-four-hour nursing care. So Dr. Mayo took himself to the only place in town where he knew he could find women "on duty" twenty-four hours a day—the Convent of the Sisters of St. Francis. Although this was an order of teaching nuns rather than a nursing order, it took Mother Alfred, the superior, just long enough to hear from Dr. Mayo that help was needed before she and her Sisters were on their way to Rommel's Dance Hall!

Mother Alfred and the Sisters of St. Francis continued to operate the nursing service until the emergency was over and the temporary hospital was closed. The nuns were congratulated on a job well done by the City fathers and thanked by grateful patients and relatives. There the whole incident would have ended if it had not been for Mother Alfred. For her, too, the whole operation had come to a successful close but, in the process, her eyes had been opened to the need for a permanent hospital. When she first approached Dr. Mayo with the suggestion that a hospital be built in Rochester, he was completely opposed to the idea and for a good reason. In those days, hospitals were little more than poorhouses for the sick who were homeless or for those who could not afford to pay for care in good nursing homes. As a result, hospitals were held in low esteem by the public and were shunned altogether by reputable physicians. Mother Alfred's answer to all this was that she and her Sisters could organize and operate a good hospital service and would even be willing to solicit the funds necessary to construct the building, if Dr. Mayo would agree to serve as medical director of the hospital and be in charge of the entire medical program. When Dr. Mayo realized that the plan being proposed was not a pious fantasy but a down-to-earth proposal by a dedicated woman who knew what she was talking about, he did an about-face and gave his wholehearted support to a venture which, two years later, culminated in the building of St. Mary's Hospital. Today, St. Mary's Hospital, which recently celebrated its eightieth anniversary, continues to provide inpatient service for Mayo Clinic patients, along with the Methodist Hospital, the city's only other voluntary hospital serving the Clinic.

The next landmark was the gradual emergence of the "Mayo Clinic." The first actual clinic operation was started at St. Mary's Hospital by Dr. Will and Dr. Charlie Mayo in 1889. They initiated it to care for surgical patients and, as it grew, the staff grew, both in numbers and in diversity of specialties. By 1906, physicians from all over the United States were visiting the "Mayo Clinic at St. Mary's Hospital" at the rate of twenty to thirty a day. They came and stood in crowded operating theaters to watch Dr. Will and Dr. Charlie as they operated on everything from goiters to gallstones, using the brilliant surgical techniques they themselves had either developed or perfected. One such visitor, Dr. George N. P. Mead from Boston, reported that together the two brothers were doing four thousand operations a year— a total that he considered "simply staggering."

The story of how the "Mayo Clinic at St. Mary's Hospital" finally became the "Mayo Clinic" is a small saga in itself. In 1909, Mrs. Maud Mellish was commissioned by the Mayos to prepare in one volume a collection of the papers written by the Mayo group, which by that time included several partners. All went well until Mrs. Mellish consulted the group about a title for the volume. It could hardly be called *The Collected Papers of Drs. Mayo, Graham, Plummer and Judd,* because that was clumsy and, besides, there were now other members in the group. The title finally agreed upon was: *Collected Papers by the Staff of St. Mary's Hospital Mayo Clinic.*

By 1912, the Mayo staff included young men in training to be doctors at the level of interns, residents, and assistants. The problem of what to call these trainees developed into an issue that was discussed at length by Dr. Will, Dr. Henry Plummer, Dr. Louis B. Wilson and the other partners. Dr. Will, who had deep convictions about democracy and equality, felt that terms like "intern" and "assistant" were demeaning and led to the kind of "yes-sir" subservience to senior staff members he had observed in house officers in some of the famous hospitals he had visited in the East. It was Dr. Wilson who finally came up with the title of "fellow," a term that was used at Oxford University. The word *fellow* came from the Middle English *felawe* and it meant comrade or companion. This seemed the perfect solution to Dr. Will and the others as well, but it led to the next question—fellows of what? They could hardly be called fellows of Drs. Mayo, Graham, Plummer and Judd! The alternate choice, "fellows of St. Mary's Hospital Mayo Clinic" was another awkward jawbreaker. The breakthrough finally came when someone suggested, "why not just fellows of the Mayo Clinic?" Thus it was that, in one fell swoop, Mayo fellows were born and the Mayo Clinic was christened!

The two final building stones in the house of Mayo took the form of buttresses to strengthen the core edifice. The first buttress was built in 1915, when the Mayo Clinic and the University of Minnesota became affiliated and jointly agreed to establish the Mayo Foundation for Medical Education and Research. As soon as the articles of agreement were signed, the Foundation began with an endowment fund of one-and-a-half million dollars, the gift of Dr. William James and Dr. Charles Horace Mayo.

The second buttress was the establishment of the nonprofit Mayo Association, in 1920. The Association was created by Dr. Will and Dr. Charlie because they believed that the potential good of the institution should in no way be hampered by individual ownership. In setting up the Association, they had "early determined that the future should be made as secure as possible by placing the clinic and all its properties, both personal and real, without reservation, in the hands of trustees, to be used for the benefit of this and future generations." Whereupon the brothers deeded all Clinic properties, consisting of real estate, stocks, bonds and other securities in the amount of some ten-and-a-half million dollars, to the Association.

Three questions remain. The first is: What about the Mayo operation as it functions today?

In 1963, the number of patients treated at the Mayo Clinic totaled some one hundred ninety thousand for the year. They came from every State in the union, from all parts of the world, from all walks of life, from all races, from all religions—and none was turned away.

As to the Foundation, today some six hundred and fifty graduate physicians elect to take their specialty training at the Mayo Clinic. In a survey carried out by the Association of American Medical Colleges, the Mayo Foundation ranked first among the twenty-five hospitals most frequently named among the places where they received residency training by part-time faculty in American medical schools. This means that the Foundation supplies more than 2 per cent of the

47

part-time medical faculty of the entire nation.

The second question is corollary to the first—namely, where are the men today who built the house of Mayo?

Dr. William Worrall Mayo died on March 6, 1911, at the age of ninety-one. Dr. William James and Dr. Charles Horace Mayo died within two months of each other in the same year, 1939, Dr. Charlie succumbing to pneumonia on May twenty-sixth, and Dr. Will to cancer on July twenty-eighth. Thus, in death as in life, it was "my brother and I"—a phrase that became the hallmark of the Mayo boys. The unique and enduring quality of the tie between the two brothers was once summed up in simple terms by Dr. Will: "From the very beginning Charlie and I always went together. We were known as the Mayo boys. Anyone that picked on one of us had the two to contend with."

There are now two Mayo doctors who bear the family name and carry on the family tradition. Dr. Charles William Mayo, the son of Dr. Charlie, after serving thirty-two years as a staff surgeon of the Mayo Clinic, recently retired at the age of sixty-five, thereby bowing to the mandatory retirement rule established by his father and his uncle. A distinguished surgeon and world citizen, Dr. "Chuck" Mayo served as an alternate delegate to the General Assembly of the United Nations under the Eisenhower administration and is currently a member of President Johnson's Commission on Heart Disease, Cancer and Stroke. Among many other honors, one of the most recent was conferred on him by Pope Paul VI, when he was designated Knight Commander of the Order of St. Sylvester.

Dr. Charles H. Mayo II, the son of Dr. "Chuck" Mayo, is following the family tradition by being trained as a surgeon at the Mayo Clinic.

The third and final question is the hardest to answer, but it is always the crucial one to a biographer forever trying to capture and describe in words that elusive will-of-the-wisp thing called the quality of soul of the man or men being sketched. It is difficult enough when the subject is alive and accessible to observation or interview; it is next to impossible when the biographee is dead.

In attempting to portray the quality of the Mayo men, the difficulty is further compounded by the fact that it covers a span of four generations.

It was by sheer luck that this biographer, in the course of searching library files, stumbled on a book entitled *Aphorisms of Dr. Charles Horace Mayo and Dr. William J. Mayo*, collected by Dr. Frederick J. Willius. The aphorisms are a distillate of the wisdom, values, ideals and aspirations of these two remarkable men and, as such, clearly reflect the quality of the hearts and souls, as well as the minds, of the men that conceived the words.

The same holds true of another item included in the appendix of this small volume. It is the so-called "Lost Oration," a speech Dr. William J. Mayo gave before a Committee of the Minnesota State Legislature, on March 22, 1917. So strong was the opposition of the medical profession to the affiliation of the University of Minnesota with the Mayo Foundation that a bill was introduced into the Minnesota State Legislature for an act to instruct the Board of Regents of the University to dissolve the affiliation. "On the night of March 22, 1917, Dr. William J. Mayo appeared before the Senate Committee on Education which was conducting public hearings on the bill. His extemporaneous remarks, set down only by the newspaper reporters present, were so powerful and so eloquent that support for the bill subsided rapidly, and it never became an act. Dr. Mayo used no manuscript. The version which follows was reproduced from the *Minneapolis Morning Tribune*, March 23, 1917, by special permission of the Minneapolis Star and Tribune Company." *

"I had some hesitancy in appearing at this meeting. There has been much misunderstanding and misapprehension about the whole plan. So that you may understand just what my brother and I desire to do, let me go back to our boyhood days.

"My father, Dr. W. W. Mayo, was recognized as the leading physician and surgeon of Southwestern Minnesota. When we were small boys we assisted him as much as we could, gradually growing into the profession much as a farmer boy learns by working with his father.

"Now my father had certain ideals. He believed that any man who had physical strength, intellectual capacity or unusual opportunity held such endowments in trust to do with them for others in proportion to his gifts.

"As our business grew, my brother and I added men to the staff, not as hired men, but as co-workers. We have had our ideals. Everyone who came into the clinic and hung up his hat was to get treatment regardless of the cost and no one was asked if he had the price.

"Because erroneous statements have been made in this regard, I will say that we have never charged a physician or a clergyman or any dependent member of the family of either.

As we grew larger, we took in young men and finally built up a school and provided fellowships to enable students of exceptional ability to work and study in connection with the clinic. We had 26 of those fellowship students in 1914, before the arrangement with the University.

"In 1898 my father retired and we took what money we had and turned it over to Burt W. Eaton, a fellow townsman, with instructions to look after it and such additions as we might make. Last

*From Aphorisms of Dr. Charles Horace Mayo (1865–1939) and Dr. William James Mayo (1861–1939), by Willius, Fredrick A., M.D. *Copyright 1951. Courtesy of Charles C. Thomas, Publisher, Springfield, Illinois.*

year it totaled about $1,500,000. It is the basis of the endowment of the foundation.

"We have never taken notes at the clinic. No mortgage has ever been given on a home to pay a bill there. We never sue. Thirty per cent of our patients are charity cases. About twenty-five per cent pay barely the cost of treatment.

"I can't understand why all this opposition should have been aroused over the affiliation with the University. It seems to be the idea of some persons that no one can want to do anything for anybody without having some sinister motive back of it.

"If we wanted money, we have it. That can't be the reason for our offer. We want the money to go back to the people who gave it to us. The proposal for this affiliation came from the University to us and did not originate with us. We want to serve the state that has given us so much and we think the best way we can serve it is through medical education.

"The offer of the endowment fund of the foundation when the affiliation becomes permanent is an outright tender despite the talk of a 'phantom gift' which has been heard through the state. I know that doctors of Minnesota two years ago were appealed to in letters containing misrepresentations.

"Now let's call a spade a spade. This money belongs to the 2,500-000 people in this state. I don't care two raps whether the medical profession of the state like the way this money has been offered for use. It wasn't their money. Discussions against the affiliation have been in the past of just such petty and trivial detail as we have heard tonight.

"I have always thought a good deal of Lincoln's Gettysburg address. There's a line in it which explains why we want to do this thing. It is 'that these dead shall not have died in vain.' We know how hard it is for those who have had the misfortune of deaths in their families, of deaths that might have been avoided. What better could we do than take young men and help them to become proficient in the profession so as to prevent needless deaths? . . .

"My brother and I are over 50 years old. What better can we do than devote our remaining years to this work?"

PAUL DUDLEY WHITE

Pioneer in Medicine and Cardiology

[1886–   ]

"'P.w.,' as he is known here, is as New England as Bunker Hill where his father was born; as Boston as the Meeting House in Roxbury where he himself grew up." * And, it might be added, as Boston as the physician who once feloniously aided and abetted Cornelia Otis Skinner to defy all the rules and regulations of English quarantine laws by spiriting her through customs with a florid case of measles! †

Up to the day in 1955 when President Dwight Eisenhower was stricken with an attack of coronary thrombosis, Paul Dudley White was a name to conjure with in medical circles all over the world, but not in the emporia of the Main Streets of the U.S.A. Within the period of hours that it took Paul White to fly from Boston to Denver, examine the President in nearby Fitzsimmons General Hospital and bring his distinguished patient back to Washington, his name had become a household word all over America. This was due not only to the fact that he was treating the President of the United States and that his name, therefore, was read or seen

*Burns, Frances: Profile of Paul White, Ike's Heart Doctor—*from the first of a series of ten articles, published by* The Boston Globe *in 1955.*

†Our Hearts Were Young and Gay, *by Cornelia Otis Skinner and Emily Kimbrough, Dodd, Mead, New York, 1942.*

52

or heard via the mass media in every town and hamlet, but also because Paul White is a born teacher. In his eyes, eager reporters and commentators, avid for answers, were just like his beloved medical students and young doctors, and so when he answered spate after spate of questions, he leaned over backward to make sure this new breed of students knew exactly what the answers meant. The result was that an extraordinary number of newsmen and ladies got an entire seminar on coronary heart disease in plain, nonmedical English for free! They, in turn, were delighted to be able to deluge the grassroots of America with their newly acquired expertise.

It is not surprising that Paul White was selected by Dwight Eisenhower's personal physician and his advisors as their choice among cardiologists to attend the President, because by 1955 he was the dean of American heart specialists and probably the only doctor whom cardiologists around the world would have acknowledged to be pre-eminent in the field.

As one colleague put it at the time, "If it had been anyone else, there would have been professional jealousy . . . but Paul's the cardiological dean—he's by way of becoming the grand old man of heart."

The "grand old man of heart" was born in Roxbury, Massachusetts, June 6, 1886, the son of Dr. Herbert Warren White and Elizabeth A. (Dudley) White.

Dr. Herbert Warren White was a horse and buggy doctor who plied his trade with pills and phylacteries for almost half a century in Roxbury, where his two sons, Paul Dudley and Joseph Warren, were born. As his sons were to do later, Dr. Herbert White graduated from the Harvard Medical

School and studied medicine abroad before he settled down to become a family doctor in Boston's South End. Stricken with a heart attack on his way to visit a patient, he died as he had lived, with stethoscope in hand, at the age of seventy-one, in 1929.

Like the Cabots, the Lodges, the Eliots and the Lowells, Paul White's forebears were among the first settlers in the Massachusetts Bay Colony. Any skeptical genealogist who insists on documentation has only to wend his way through parts of Boston's South End and look up at two street signs, one marked "Dudley," the other, "Warren," for evidence. Paul White's mother was Elizabeth Dudley, the descendant of a long line of Vermont and Massachusetts Dudleys. Both his father and an uncle, Dr. Franklin Warren White, bore the middle name of another illustrious ancestor, General Joseph Warren, the hero of Bunker Hill.

Dr. Herbert White was for many years one of the deacons of the Dudley Street Baptist Church. He was a vigorous man whose chief attributes were a strong sense of duty, great energy and firm self-discipline. Some of these qualities were undoubtedly inherited by his older son, because Paul White's energy has been legendary ever since his internship days at the Massachusetts General Hospital, where he acquired the reputation of getting through his work faster than any other "pup" intern on the entire medical service! His ability to organize his time with self-disciplined efficiency is such that he can do in one day what an ordinary man would need a month to do. It could be argued psychologically that his ability to set limits on himself and organize his time to include activities other than work might represent an unconscious protest against the kind of life his father led. He once said, "Having seen how hard Father worked, always being called

54

out day and night, with never an uninterrupted dinner party, concert or theater, both my brother and I early decided we'd never be doctors— Now Warren is an orthopedic surgeon in Honolulu and here I am!"

As a small boy, Paul spent a great deal of time with his father. During the six years he attended the Boys' Latin School in Roxbury, his after-school hours and his Saturdays were passed in making house calls with his father. Although he was undersized and slightly built, he learned to manage his father's horse and carriage at an early age, so he was entrusted with the post of coachman on his father's rounds.

It is worth pausing to note that what other boys his age might have considered a tiresome chore, he chose to accept as a challenge. This way of reacting to demands above and beyond his age, size and apparent physical capacity is one of Paul White's lifelong key characteristics. Whether it was expressed in terms of "the pup intern who got through his work faster than anyone ever had done before or since," or the adult mountain climber who "ran up" Mount Chocorua in New Hampshire with a temperature of 101°, or the eminent dean of cardiologists who led an expedition to the Bering Sea in pursuit of the heart beat of a Beluga white whale, his pattern of response to demand or challenge has always been the same. Instead of being on standby, ready to cope with stresses as they might emerge, he elected to meet them in advance, with the time, place and action chosen by him and *not* dictated by the circumstances of his environment.

When he graduated from the Roxbury Latin School, Paul was too young for college, so he spent a year of study on his own before he entered Harvard College in 1904. Because his interest had been aroused during his preparatory school years in such subjects as history, literature, Greek and Latin, he entered Harvard with the intention of becoming a teacher of history and the classics. It wasn't until he reached his junior year in college that he became enchanted with science and medicine to the extent that he switched his major to zoology and combined his senior year at Harvard College with his first year of medicine at the Harvard Medical School.

He graduated from the Harvard Medical School in 1911. After spending those two unforgettable internship years at the Massachusetts General Hospital as the fastest pup on the medical service, he was selected by the chief of service, Dr. David Edsall, as one of his "brightest buttons," to be sent abroad for further study on a traveling fellowship.

Paul White's career in research, practice and teaching in the field of heart disease really began when he enrolled as a graduate student at the University College Hospital Medical School, London (1913–14). It was during this year of study that he met with and worked in the laboratory of the great Scottish-English physiologist, Sir James MacKenzie.

It was also during this time that he first learned how to use an electrocardiograph machine and interpret the tracings of the heart it produced. He became so intrigued with this model-T version of the modern, streamlined EKG machine that he brought it back from Cambridge when he returned to Boston and installed it in the basement of the old Bulfinch Building at the Massachusetts General Hospital. There, over a period of seventeen years, the machine remained a source of pride and joy to him but also a cause of despair because he spent more than half his time repairing its frequent breakdowns. In spite of repeated mechanical difficulties, however, over the seventeen-year period, 21,160 cardiograms were made on this historic machine and the original glass plates on which it recorded the first Boston heartbeat are still on file among Paul White's most prized possessions.

On his return from Europe, he finished his residency in medicine at the Massachusetts General Hospital, where he started as an assistant and rose to become full consultant in medicine and chief of the cardiac service in 1920, a post he held until his retirement. His parallel rise in academic medicine began with his appointment as teaching fellow at the Harvard Medical School in 1914 and culminated with his promotion to clinical professor of medicine in 1920.

In 1931, he published the first edition of his book, *Heart Disease*, which has since become the standard classic textbook in cardiology. It is now in its fourth edition. His other published works include, *Heart Disease in General Practice* (1937); *Electrocardiography in Practice*, with Ashton Graybill (1941); *Coronary Heart Disease in Young Adults*, with Menard M. Gertler (1954); *Clues in the Diagnosis and Treatment of Heart Disease* (1955, 1st ed.; 1956, 2nd ed.); *Rehabilitation of the Cardiovascular Patient* (1958); and, most recently, *Fitness for the Whole Family* (1964). He himself considers that, of all the many books and articles he has written, his most important scientific contribution was made in 1921, when he published, together with Dr. Merrill Myers of Iowa, an original article on "The Classification of Cardiac Diagnosis," in the *Journal* of the American Medical Association.

In his research on heartbeat range which he has conducted for almost fifty years, he has studied and established heartbeat frequencies in various animals, including mice, an elephant and the aforementioned Beluga white whale! Not long ago he headed another expedition in an effort to record the heartbeat of the gray whale, a dangerous fifty-ton giant that runs off the California coast. Although this venture ended in failure, it has not dimmed the spectacular success of the first expedition nor Paul White's determination to have another try, if he can ever find time in his present busy life.

Like many of his New England forebears before him, Paul White has always been a restless wanderer over the face of the earth, and so, by inheritance and inclination, he is an internationalist at heart. His first return to Europe after his year in England as a Harvard traveling fellow was in 1919, when he went to Greece with the Greek Medical Commission of the American Red Cross to bring medical aid and supplies to the Balkans.

Since that initial mission to Greece, Dr. White has made innumerable visits to European countries as a participant in teaching missions supported by various philanthropic organizations. After World War II, he took part in two teaching missions sponsored by the Unitarian Service Committee. The first was a mission to Czechoslovakia, in 1946. He was chairman of the group of doctors which included, among others, Dr. Joseph Aub and Dr. Otto Krayer of Harvard and Drs. Volker and Lazansky of Tufts. Because Europe had been bled dry of medical supplies during the war, they took with them surgical supplies, X-ray equipment and drugs, as well as medical books and journals. This traveling faculty of fourteen distinguished internists, surgeons and other specialists managed to give lectures, see patients and give consultation to individual doctors in their whirlwind tour of medical schools, hospitals and clinics that covered an area of some twenty-four hundred miles! A while after their return to the States, the fourteen doctors were awarded Czechoslovakia's highest honor, the Order of the White Lion. In making the presentation in Washington, D.C., Ambassador Juraj Slavik termed the Unitarian mission, "The most important work for health and rehabilitation which is being done in the world at present."

In 1948, the second Unitarian Service Committee mission was sent to Greece. This time, Paul White, as a member of a second distinguished group of physicians, was returning to a country which he loved and which loved him. In Greece, the Czech experience was repeated with another whirlwind round of lectures, consultations and patients. The only difference this time was that, at the conclusion of the Greek tour instead of returning home, the group flew to Italy, where they gave a duplicate performance up and down the Italian peninisula, taking time out only to attend an audience with the Pope.

For his contributions to the people of Greece, Paul White was twice decorated by the Greek government. He was also awarded honorary degrees by the University of Athens and Salonica University.

Since 1948, the peripatetic New England cardiologist has been on teaching missions to Pakistan, India, Israel, the U.S.S.R., and Greece, for the third time. He has won international recognition for his work in teaching, research and practice in the form of honorary degrees, memberships in international societies and awards of various kinds from all parts of the globe.

In addition to the honorary degrees he holds from the two universities in Greece, Dr. White is the recipient of degrees from Charles University, in Prague, Czechoslovakia, the University of Montreal, the University of Brazil and, in his own country, from the University of Southern California, Harvard University and Ithaca College.

He holds membership in the National Academy of Medicine of France, The Royal Society of Medicine (England), the Cardiac Society of Great Britain and Ireland, and the Soviet Academy of Medical Sciences. He belongs to cardiology societies of France, Mexico, Czechoslovakia, Brazil, Chile, South Africa, Australia, Italy, Belgium and Argentina. In the United States, he served as chairman of the committee on cardiovascular disease of the National Research Council from 1940–46 and as Executive Director of the National Advisory Heart Council from 1948–56. He is past president of the American Heart Association, past president of the International Society of Cardiology and present president of the International Society of Cardiology Foundation. He received the Lasker Award of the American Heart Association and the American Medical Association's Distinguished Service Medal for outstanding achievement in the field of cardiovascular disease. In 1951, he was decorated by the government of France with the Legion of Honor.

What about Paul White today? What are the present activities of a man who has "lived three lives" in his nearly eighty years? By all rights and in keeping with the quaint notions of current mores, he should be spending his retirement years "enjoying" a life of ease with a few old cronies in one of the clubs he belongs to in Boston or in puttering about his house in Belmont or on his farm in Harvard, Massachusetts. The fact of the matter is that he is leading a very active professional and personal life.

When he is in Boston, Dr. White conducts the Cardiac Teaching Clinic at the Massachusetts General Hospital on Tuesday mornings from 10:30 to 12:00. On Thursdays, he attends medical grand rounds and on Fridays, cardiac rounds at the same hospital. Sandwiched in between these fixed routines, he gives lectures to students and staff, sees old patients, and continues his research on the basic causes of heart disease. Since he has commitments all over the world, he makes frequent flying trips abroad to attend meetings, give lectures, act as consultant when requested and represent the United States on a variety of committees and commissions. And every once in a while he takes off on a flying junket of his own in pursuit of yet another whale!

As to his home life, Paul White likes nothing better than to spend an evening reading aloud with his wife such books as *Scrolls from the Dead Sea* or the latest archeological report on the results of current diggings at Knossus, Crete. Or if they happen to be at their farm in Harvard, instead of in their living room in Belmont, the weekend visitor is likely to find Paul White in flannel shirt and old slacks, chopping wood, while Mrs. White cuts flowers for the dining table.

Paul White met Ina Reid during the course of a teaching stint he undertook at Smith College, in Northampton, Massachusetts. She was taking postgraduate training in psychiatric social work at Smith at the same time. Following a brief courtship, they were married in 1924. The Whites have two grown children: Penelope Dudley (Mrs. Robert Nock) and Alexander Warren.

It was my misfortune not to be able to arrange an interview with Dr. White during the preparation of this manuscript. In response to my letter suggesting the possible dates when I could come to Boston, he wrote that he would be in Europe throughout the time I specified in my letter and, therefore, regretted he wouldn't be able to see me.

The letter Paul White wrote me was so characteristically simple and warm, it brought back a flood of memories to one who had been part of a group of "young doctors" who "audited" Paul White's teaching seminars way back in the late thirties. The word "audited" is put in quotes because the half dozen or so of us who managed to get to his teaching clinics or attend his rounds as often as possible were not on his service nor were we officially signed up as postgraduate students in cardiology. Each of us was a Harvard fellow, doing postgraduate work in entirely different fields—one, for example, was a research fellow in obstetrics, working at the Boston Lying-in Hospital. Another was a budding virologist, working at the Boston City Hospital. A third was actually carrying out a research project at the Massachusetts General Hospital, but *not* in cardiology. As for me, I was officially a research fellow in pediatrics, doing my work at the Boston Children's Hospital. The single bond we had in common was Paul White and we "worshiped at his feet." Although each of us was committed to a different area of medicine and impatient to get there as fast as possible, we had sense enough to pause in our pursuit to sit at the feet of one of the truly "greats" of medicine. We were responding to the magic of the really great teacher who, regardless of subject, kindles a fire in a student that glows steadily, bursts into flame or barely flickers—but, for the rest of his life, never goes out.

JOHN CLARE WHITEHORN

Pioneer in Psychiatric Research and Education

[1894–   ]

I⊤ SEEMS ironic—but curiously fitting—that the man who became the Henry Phipps Professor of Psychiatry at Johns Hopkins and who was *not* a psychiatrist should be the same man who was born in a town that *never* existed.

In his listing in *Who's Who in America*,* John Clare Whitehorn's birthplace is given as Spencer, Nebraska. In actual fact, he was born in Rochester, Nebraska, which was not a town but a post office on the banks of the Niobrara River, in Boyd County. It so happened that the postmistress of Rochester was John Whitehorn's mother and the post office, the Whitehorn homestead. His father had "homesteaded" to Boyd County after his business failed and he went bankrupt. In those days, "homesteaders" could buy land from the government for a dollar an acre. If they could make a go of it for three years, the land became theirs. And so it was that John Whitehorn came to be born, not in Spencer but at a "freighter" † outpost on the Niobrara River, in Boyd County, Nebraska, on December 6, 1894.

*Who's Who in America, *published by A. N. Marquis—Vol. 33, 1964-65.*
†*"Freighters" were covered wagons drawn by six horses. They preceded the railroad which came into Boyd County in 1904.*

The reason why John Whitehorn chose to study medicine is not completely clear to him even today. He might just as easily have become a writer or a teacher, because he worked his way through high school and college, first as a printer and later as a teacher.

Printing and writing fascinated him from the moment he learned the alphabet as a small boy by spelling out the markings on the potbelly stove in the kitchen of his home. When his family moved to town and he began elementary school in a one-room schoolhouse, he made two important discoveries —one, that he was bright in comparison with the other children, and two, that if he kept his ears open, he could pick up pearls of knowledge by "auditing" the more advanced lessons being taught to older children in the same room.

By the time he was eighteen, John was majoring in philosophy at Doane College, in Crete, Nebraska, teaching Sunday school and high school, running a Boy Scout troop as an assistant scoutmaster (he was too young to qualify as a scoutmaster) and playing college football! In retrospect, he says of his adolescent years, "I must have been obnoxious to many people because I was so serious and so earnest." * But, in the same breath, he says, "I really enjoyed playing football all through college," and, "I made the team, even though I only weighed one hundred and thirty-five pounds," and finally, with characteristic irony, "but then it was only a small college!" To a biographer, two qualities which John Whitehorn was to extol much later in his writings seem already clearly visible in him before adolescence, namely, the ability to "tolerate uncertainty" and to take on one's share of responsibility as a human being.

*Personal interview with author in July 1964.

Dr. Howard A. Rusk, pioneer in Rehabilitation

Dr. William C. Menninger, one of the pioneers in the development of a
Community Mental Health Program

Photograph by Earl Seubert.
Copyright 1964 by Medical World Publishing Co., Inc.

Dr. Charles W. Mayo, standing before a statue of his father and uncle.
Together they founded the famed clinic pioneering Group Practice
in Medicine

Courtesy of Harvard University

Dr. Benjamin Spock, pioneer in Baby and Child Care

Dr. Martha May Eliot, pioneer in Public Health and Maternal and Child Health

Scurlock

Dr. William Montague Cobb, pioneer in Anatomy and Medical Anthropology

Dr. Paul Dudley White, pioneer in Medicine and Cardiology

Leonard W. Grief, Jr.

Dr. John Clare Whitehorn, pioneer in Psychiatric Research and Education

Dr. Anna Freud, pioneer in Psychoanalysis and Child Therapy

The National Foundation—March of Dimes

Irene Shwachman

Eleven of the seventeen people nominated to the Polio Hall of Fame at the Georgia Warm Springs Foundation stand before their busts at the dedication ceremonies in January, 1958. Reading left to right, are Dr. Thomas M. Rivers, Dr. Charles Armstrong, Dr. John R. Paul, Dr. Thomas Francis, Jr., Dr. Albert B. Sabin, Dr. Joseph L. Melnick, Dr. Isabel Morgan, Dr. Howard A. Howe, Dr. David Bodian, and Dr. Jonas Salk. Mrs. Franklin D. Roosevelt stands at the right with Basil O'Connor, under the bust of her late husband. Busts of deceased scientists are at extreme left of photograph. Dr. John F. Enders, whose illness prevented him from attending, is shown in picture at right.

Dr. Alfred Blalock   Dr. Helen Taussig

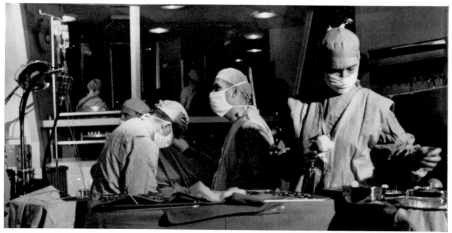

The Surgery Story

Two incidents which he remembers from his childhood seem particularly relevant. One was a spelling bee which he won by "spelling down" his fellow pupils, most of whom were older and some of them towering six-footers. To one who was small, slight and nicknamed "Cottontop," because his hair was as white as cotton, this kind of public performance was always embarrassing and so, even when he won, he was left with a feeling of discomfort rather than pleasure. The important thing to note, however, is that he managed to tolerate this feeling of uneasiness and to face up to the responsibility of classroom competition, rather than run away from it.

The other incident occurred when he was twelve. One day when he was playing "cowboys and Indians," he was accidentally shot in the eye by another boy with a BB gun. The BB ball went right through the lens of one eye and if surgery, like the railroad, had not yet come to Nebraska, he would have lost the sight in that eye completely. As it happened, a good surgeon had settled in Omaha and, thanks to his skill, the sight was saved, but not the lens. To this day, John Whitehorn carries the mark of that early accident in the form of "heterochromia," which means that the iris of the injured eye is different in color from that in the good eye. He also has some limitation of vision in the bad eye, which he compensates for by cocking his head. In commenting on how he felt at the time of the injury, he says that his mother and father were shocked and deeply troubled over his possible loss of vision, because they were afraid any limitation of vision might interfere with the scholarly academic career toward which he seemed headed. His concern over his parents' anxiety was such that his own did not seem to register.

Moreover, whatever apprehension he might have felt over possible loss of vision at the time did not seem to carry with it forebodings about his future.

John Whitehorn entered the Harvard Medical School in 1917 on a scholarship which he had applied for and won in stiff competition with graduates of the more favored Ivy League colleges. When I asked why he had applied only to Harvard, he answered, "Because Harvard offered the highest paying scholarships and I had no money—I even had to borrow money to get to Boston." He now feels he was unduly brash in sending a letter along with his application, announcing that he was coming to Boston to enter the medical school on the assumption that he would be accepted. By way of explanation, he had written his baccalaureate thesis on the subject of measuring the mass of an electron and this had been both published in a journal and reprinted in *The Scientific American*. He now believes that the reprint he enclosed with his application to Harvard counteracted the effect of his naive letter and, in large measure, accounted for his being awarded the scholarship.

He put himself through Harvard by studying night and day to qualify for a scholarship for each of the three succeeding years he needed to complete his medical education. When he took his degree in 1921, he not only graduated *cum laude* but he was already launched on a career in research, having worked in the laboratory with the famous biochemist, Dr. Otto Folin.

In 1921, John Whitehorn married Jeannette Miller of Fairmont, Nebraska. They had three children: a son Richard, who is now an electronics engineer in Palo Alto, California; a daughter Joan, who is the wife of S. T. Boggs, an anthropologist, of Kensington, Maryland; and another son Alfred, who was killed in battle in Germany in World War II. After the children were grown up, Mrs. Whitehorn had an interesting and successful career as a medical artist. At the present writing, the Whitehorns have seven grandchildren.

It was Dr. Folin who encouraged Dr. Whitehorn to take a job which was open at the McLean Hospital in Waverly, Massachusetts. McLean Hospital was then and still is, a topflight private psychiatric hospital, affiliated, in one way or another, with most of the medical schools in the Boston area. The hospital wanted a well-trained physician to head up its laboratory department, to supervise the routine laboratory work and also to initiate a research program, using biochemical and physiological techniques for the study of psychiatric illness.

John Whitehorn went to work at McLean right after his graduation from Harvard in 1921 and he stayed there seventeen years. How he gradually developed into a unique kind of psychotherapist from his starting point as a strictly scientific, research biochemist over that seventeen-year period is best explained in his own words.

"My own personal introduction to the possible therapeutic value of psychologic influences occurred in a situation which may seem strange to this group. I was working in a biochemical laboratory and had chosen to study certain aspects of the energy metabolism involving carbohydrates and phosphates. I must remind you that those were primitive days in biochemistry, a generation ago. I did all the work myself— the determinations of blood sugar and of inorganic phosphates, the administration of solutions of glucose and of sodium acid phosphate to the subjects, the collection of blood specimens from the subjects, and so forth. The subjects were schizophrenic patients, with whom I became fairly well acquainted by these necessities of my work. There was, I thought, some reason to hope that these patients, who appeared quite listless and lacking in energy, in the personal sense, might become more energetic, in the personal sense, by the experimental manipulation of the biochemical mechanisms of energy transformations. This was before the time of the insulin-shock therapy, and my experimental procedure was aimed at producing abrupt hyperglycemia and rapid hexosephosphorylation. It was quite exciting when my clinical colleagues saw evidence of clinical improvement in my subjects, greater than would otherwise have been expected. Various control studies were then undertaken, for example, the administration of phosphate without glucose, which produced very interesting and unexpectedly complicated results, biochemically, but not much clinical effect. I also ran a control series which consisted only of conversation, without glucose or phosphate. It was facetiously suggested by some that this meant the substitution of sweet talk for glucose, but that was not a very close analogy. The conversations were sharper than would be implied by such a metaphorical statement. They more nearly resembled the acid phosphate than the glucose.

"In the original experimental procedures, a certain amount of casual conversation had arisen during my frequent personal contacts with my subjects, usually some bantering comments about venepuncture, the sharpness of the needle, the possibility of learning from a small blood sample about what goes on inside of oneself, and the like. The control series of conversations much resembled these, beginning casually but becoming more earnest. It did turn out that in the conversational control series greater clinical improvement was observed than in any of the experimental series. This was not completely unexpected. Perhaps this conversational control series would not have been undertaken had it not happened that several of the improving patients in the original experiments had sought me out to express appreciation, and commented upon the value to them of the apparently casual talks we had had.

"It was in the way I have just described that I found myself presented with a new problem: to understand how some patients had found conversations favorable to their improvement. It became a matter of great interest to me to study the early stages of improvement, and to seek to understand how the patients found help in conversations, some of them rather odd conversations. Newcomers to the hospital situation, not knowing the experimental background, called these activities psychotherapy. At first I demurred from such a designation, but later quit arguing against it.

"The general inquisitive orientation personally developed through these experiences has remained with me, and I find myself still inclined to view what people call psychotherapy in a different perspective than most people do. I see the patient as potentially capable of recovery or improvement, and as making use at times of some aspects of his interactions with his physician as aids in his recovery process. I think that I do not, in this formulation, overmodestly undervalue the physician's contribution to the recovery process. I would say that for many patients this assistance seems crucially necessary. But I look upon psychotherapy in this perspective as a partnership task—as one aspect of the care of the patient— not as something done to the patient.

"The situation which I have just described was the beginning, not the end of my psychotherapeutic education. I have learned some since then. But the general orientation persists." *

*Whitehorn, J. C.: "Types of Leadership Involved in Psychotherapy," American Journal of Psychotherapy, Vol. XVI, No. 3, 366–378, July 1962.

In 1932, Dr. Whitehorn wrote a paper on "Instinct and Emotions," in which he formulated for the first time a theoretical concept of human behavior based on his observations of and "conversations" with mentally ill patients. With the publication of this paper he won professional recognition as a clinical psychiatrist and from that time on his rise to the heights of the psychiatric ladder was phenomenal. In 1938, he was appointed professor of psychiatry at the Washington University School of Medicine in St. Louis, Missouri, and Psychiatrist-in-Chief at Barnes Hospital, St. Louis. During the three years he was at Washington University, Whitehorn fully developed and taught the basic theories of human behavior in illness and in health that he had formed during his seventeen years of psychiatric research, treatment and teaching at McLean Hospital and the Harvard Medical School. He believes that he reached the critical turning point in his career in St. Louis because, by the time he was appointed the Henry C. Phipps Professor of Psychiatry and director of the department of Psychiatry at Johns Hopkins, in Baltimore, Maryland, in 1941, he was fully committed to the idea that human behavior can be better understood in terms of "attitudes" rather than of instincts.

The corollary to this new approach of assessing people or patients in terms of their attitudes and not instincts was that, in order to find out how patients felt about this, that or the other, you had *to ask them*. And so a new way of interviewing psychiatric patients by "seeing and treating them as human beings without catchwords, slogans or jargon" was introduced by John Whitehorn and it represents his greatest contribution to American psychiatry.

If St. Louis was the turning point in Whitehorn's career,

his nineteen years at Johns Hopkins were its culmination. It was during the latter years that he taught medical students and young doctors how to "see and treat patients as human beings," by example rather than precept.

It was also during the Hopkins years that he carried out a number of research studies on schizophrenic patients, the most important of which was a systematic study of doctors working with schizophrenic patients.

In collaboration with Dr. Barbara Betz, a study was made of two groups of doctors treating schizophrenic patients with markedly different results. The patients of the one group of doctors (group A) showed an improvement rate of 75 per cent, while the patients of the other doctor group (group B) had an improvement rate of only 27 per cent. This striking contrast led Whitehorn and Betz to investigate the differences between the two groups of doctors themselves.

They came to the conclusion, which they reported in a paper in 1954,* that the outstanding difference was in the types of leadership exerted by the two groups. The doctors in group B, whose patients responded poorly, were found to be "passive permissive," or what one might call spectator-observers. The doctors in group A, on the other hand, were "active personal participants" in the treatment of their patients, giving needed support of sympathy and bolstering the patient's self-esteem but also very clearly setting limits on what kind of behavior would be tolerated and what would not. If documentation were needed to support Whitehorn's thesis, derived from his experience at McLean, that psychotherapy is a partnership task between doctor and patient and

*Whitehorn, J. C., and Betz, Barbara: "The Relationship of the Therapist to the Outcome of Therapy in Schizophrenia," Psychiatric Research Reports, No. 5, American Psychiatric Association, 1956, 89.

not a one-sided "doing something" to a patient on the part of the doctor, this brilliant research study really nailed it down.

In addition to his outstanding contributions in the areas of psychiatric research and training over a period of some thirty-five years, John Whitehorn devoted an enormous amount of his time and energy to the advancement of psychiatry as an organization. He was a member of the American Board of Psychiatry and Neurology from 1943 to 1949, and during the years 1946, 1948 and 1949, he served as president of the Board. From 1954 to 1958, he was a member of the National Advisory Mental Health Council to the Surgeon General, USPHS. Between 1949 and 1951, he served successively as president-elect, president, and finally member of the Council of the American Psychiatric Association.

His contributions to the State of Maryland, where he has lived ever since coming to Johns Hopkins in 1941, have been no less impressive than his efforts at the national level. From 1950 to 1960, he served as Chairman of the State Mental Health Advisory Board and from 1953 to 1960 he was a member of the Executive Committee of the Medical Care Committee of the State of Maryland. And, although he retired as professor and head of the department of psychiatry at Johns Hopkins in 1960, he was appointed by the Governor to the Maryland Board of Health and Mental Hygiene in 1961 and he continues to serve as vice-chairman of the Board at the present time.

Among the many honors conferred on Dr. Whitehorn, particularly noteworthy are his being named: Honorary Associate Physician to Guy's Hospital, London, 1948 (to present); member of the War Department Commission to Combat Exhaustion, E.T.O., 1945, and recipient of the Emil

Gutheil Medal by the American Association for the Advancement of Psychotherapy, 1961.

A prolific writer since his early college days, John Whitehorn's published papers, lectures and other writings now number over one hundred and twenty-five. He has also been a member of the editorial board of the *American Journal of Psychiatry* (1942–62), the editorial board of *Medicine* (1956–present) and the editorial council of the *International Journal of Social Psychiatry*.

One has only to do a chronological review of the titles listed in his lengthy bibliography to be a witness to a scientist-physician's "pilgrim's progress." Beginning with his first published paper, entitled *The Nature of Matter* * (the reprint of which won him the scholarship to Harvard), one can follow the bench marks in his process of maturation. The following titles of articles and dates of publication tell their own story:

Simplified Method for the Determination of Chlorides in Blood, 1921

The Relation Between Stature and the Latent Period of the Knee Jerk, 1930

The Material in the Hands of the Biochemist, 1935

Attempts to Teach Principles of Psychiatric Interviewing, 1941

Combat Exhaustion, 1942

Guide to Interviewing and Clinical Personality Study, 1944

The Concepts of "Meaning" and "Cause" in Psychodynamics, 1947

Psychiatry and Human Values, 1955

Studies of the Doctor as a Crucial Factor for the Prog-

---

*Whitehorn, John C.: "The Nature of Matter"—Scientific American Supplement, LXXXIV (1917) 82 and 106.

nosis of Schizophrenic Patients, 1960
The Doctor's Image of Man, 1961
Alienation and Leadership, 1961
Education for Uncertainty, 1961

One of Dr. Whitehorn's most brilliant essays was alluded to early in this sketch. It was presented at the celebration of the one hundred fiftieth anniversary of the Massachusetts General Hospital, in February 1961, published under the provocative title: *Education for Uncertainty.* The keynote of the address is to be found in the following paragraph:

One cannot become aware of alternatives without some ability to tolerate uncertainty, and one cannot exercise good judgment and common sense in reaching well considered conclusions and wise action unless one can tolerate anxiety with equanimity. Frightened and over-anxious awareness of uncertainty is of little use for it hinders the operation of good judgment.*

Although Dr. Whitehorn has continued to write articles for psychiatric journals subsequently, this essay represents the finished product in the growth and development of a great and remarkable man who happened over time to put all of his extraordinary talents and energy to use for people in the field of psychiatry.

Whitehorn J. C.: "Education for Uncertainty." Reprinted for private circulation from Perspectives in Biology and Medicine, *Vol. VII, No. 1, 118–123, Autumn, 1963.*

BENJAMIN SPOCK
Pioneer in Baby and Child Care
[1903–   ]

*B*aby and Child Care, by Dr. Benjamin Spock, the most widely recommended and read handbook for parents ever published, has sold 16,000,000 copies!

The revised and enlarged paperback edition, published by Pocket Books, Inc., in April 1964, carries the following information:

> BABY AND CHILD CARE—A *Giant Cardinal* edition
> 1st printing .... May 1946
> 133rd printing .... April 1964

> This book is a new version of *The Pocket Book of Baby and Child Care*, originally published under the title *The Common Sense Book of Baby and Child Care by Duell, Sloan & Pearce.*

> In its previous paper-bound editions, Dr. Spock's book had 58 printings and is *the best-selling new title issued in the United States since 1895, when best-seller lists began.*

The above words were put in italics, not by the publisher, but by this author as an expression of awe and wonder at holding in her hand a copy (and an autographed one at that) of the top best seller of all best-selling new books since 1895! That *Baby and Child Care* has long been a best seller is

75

knowledge I share in common with 179,999,999 million other Americans, but the fact that it is *the* best seller of all time, this particular American did *not* know.

The author of *Baby and Child Care* is as far removed from babies in physical appearance as he is close to them intellectually and emotionally. He is six-feet-fourish in height, lean and rangy in build, with the kind of blue eyes, tanned skin and outdoor look of a seaman (which he is) or a varsity crewman (which he was).

The descriptive adjectives I scribbled in my notes read, "tall, laughing, warm man" followed by "marvelous sense of humor: a Benchley-type talent for taking off the solemn and stodgy with devastating accuracy."

Before my interview * with Dr. Spock, he was kind enough to send me a copy of a short autobiographical sketch he had written for his publishers entitled, *Brief Autobiography of Benjamin McLane Spock*. After the interview, I did a re-run of his sketch as a check against my notes and used a tape recorder to dictate his words, amplified by my rough notes. When I played back my first tape, what came out, to my surprise, was an exercise in counterpoint which would never have emerged if the lines had been written rather than spoken.

What follows is a somewhat edited version of the original tape recording.

"I was born May 2, 1903, in New Haven, Connecticut, the oldest of the six children of Benjamin Ives Spock (for many years General Counsel of the New Haven Railroad) and Mildred Stoughton Spock. Three of my four sisters have been in teaching or psychology and my brother is a schoolteacher."

Personal interview with author in September, 1964.

BENJAMIN SPOCK

COMMENT

In answer to my question—"What in your early childhood years influenced your choice of career?" Dr. Spock said that, as the oldest of six children, he had to look after the younger children. He believes the first child in a family probably solves sibling rivalry by becoming a parent. Thinks this is what he did. Tells with wry humor about his mother's bridling when he, after he was grown up, asked her about jealousy and her vigorous retort, "Thank goodness, no child of mine ever showed the slightest trace of jealousy."

The Spocks were a child-centered family. Father, counsel for New York, New Haven and Hartford Railroad, had office close enough to come home every day for lunch. He was very much a family man—no club life, no "pals." Father was *father* of family and mother was *mother* of family. On Sundays the whole family went out for a ride in the car.

Mother frowned on nursemaids (still does). Wouldn't even play cards when children were small but later became crack bridge player!

Choice of career of all six children reflects family preoccupation with children. Each one picked a "caretaking" profession, i.e., two sisters are schoolteachers, one sister a Ph.D. in psychology, younger sister worked as researcher at Yale School of Alcohol Studies.

"I graduated from Phillips Academy, Andover, in 1921, and from Yale College with a B.A. in 1925. (I rowed on the Yale crew which won in the 1924 Olympic Games in Paris.) I attended the Yale Medical School for two years, then transferred in 1927 to the College of Physicians and Surgeons, Columbia University, from which I received the M.D. degree in 1929.

"I had an internship in medicine at the Presbyterian Hospital, New York, 1929-31, a pediatric residency at New York

Nursery and Child's Hospital, 1931–32, and a psychiatric residency at New York Hospital, 1932–33.

"From 1933 to 1947 (except for two years in the Navy), I practiced pediatrics with a special interest in its psychological aspects. At the same time, I served, part-time, on the pediatric and psychiatric staff of Cornell Medical College and New York Hospital, and was school physician at the Brearly School. I took training at the New York Psychoanalytic Institute, was on the teaching staff of the New York City Health Department and the Institute on Personality Development."

COMMENT

Spock attributes his special interest in the psychological aspects of pediatrics to his feeling of discomfort about counseling parents without knowing "any of the answers." No one knew answers to psychological questions those days and no one had written anything. This is reason he took year's residency in psychiatry and began training in psychoanalysis at same time he started practice. Still remembers first five years of practice as painful experience because he had to learn by trial and error method. Thinks his having to learn the hard way ultimately led to his writing books for parents.

"I married Jane Cheney of South Manchester, Connecticut, in 1927, and we had two children, born in New York— Michael, in 1933 (who is married, has two sons, and is Director of the Children's Museum in Boston), and John, in 1944, who is attending Harvard College.

"From 1944 to 1946 I was a lieutenant comamnder, U.S. Naval Reserve, serving as a psychiatrist in naval hospitals in New York and California."

COMMENT

Spock spent most of two years in Navy in charge of psychopathic wards but for a few months, served as pediatrician on newborn nursery. Found this golden opportunity to test out some pet theories on baby care while writing first edition of *Baby and Child Care*. One example—he put eighty-five per cent of the newborns in nursery on breast feeding. Results were excellent. Mothers liked nursing babies if given encouragement and support; babies thrived.

"After one more year of pediatric practice in New York, I joined, in 1947, the staff of the Rochester (Minnesota) Child Health Institute which was working out a program of physical and psychological health for the children of the city. I was also on the staff of the Mayo Clinic, as consultant in psychiatry, and the faculty of the University of Minnesota."

COMMENT

Spock took Rochester job because he saw it as wonderful opportunity to work with exciting group of people on Rochester Child Health Project, financed by Mayos, headed by Dr. C. Anderson Aldrich, pediatrician—author of *Babies Are Human Beings*.

Group was to do a study on how to set up a model child-care program (mental and physical) for entire city of Rochester. Included in group were experts from child-related disciplines—psychologists, psychiatrists, pediatricians, nurses, social workers, teachers, child welfare worker, etc., etc. Total emphasis of study was directed toward prevention, i.e., to come up with ways to detect earliest signs of illness or trouble and *prevent*.

Spock already sold on this approach from earlier experience in New York. When on staff of Institute on Personality Development run by Caroline Zachary, an educator, had met once a week with multi-disciplined staff for case conference. Discovered psychiatric treatment *not* necessary for most kids if teacher, psychologist, pediatrician, etc., discussed case together and chipped in on solution to kid's problem *before* he got seriously disturbed or in trouble.

Rochester Child Health Project finished after four years (1947–51) but service program never got off ground. Aldrich died of cancer in 1949. Project might have weathered this blow but couldn't survive withdrawal of Mayo financial support in '51. Mayo people felt program recommended by study group "too expensive." Spock agrees service would have been high cost but worth it. Believes Mayos never really oriented toward preventive medicine. From earliest beginnings, Mayo Clinic doctors focused on diagnosis and treatment of ailments already present. Money and skills have been poured into developing high-powered new surgical and medical techniques.*

"In 1951 I went to organize a teaching program in child psychiatry and child development at the University of Pittsburgh Medical School."

COMMENT

Spock was attracted to University of Pittsburgh by opportunity to set up a combined department as new venture. As first professor of Child Development and Child Psychiatry in medical school, had access to four cooperating units for training students:

a well baby clinic run by city health department—
a nursery school for graduate students run by university—
the pediatric department of the medical school
the division of child psychiatry at Children's Hospital.

Stayed long enough to get good teaching program off and running over tough administrative hurdles. Mission completed in 1955.

"Since 1955 I have been Professor of Child Development at Western Reserve University, in Cleveland, principally as a teacher in the revised curriculum which gives the students experience with patients from the first year of medical school; † also as director of a study of child rearing."

COMMENT

In answer to question—"Does revised curriculum turn out better

*See page 40, "The Men of Mayo, Pioneers in the Group Practice of Medicine," in this book.

†In traditional medical curriculum still operant in majority of United States medical schools, students do not start working with patients until their third year.—Author's note.

80

students?"—Spock's answer was emphatic "Yes." Believes that being assigned to a family in very first year has humanizing effect on student. Student responsible for "his family" throughout four years. Sees family in WRU Family Clinic, makes home visits, finally becomes family doctor.

Spock thinks student's defense against stresses faced during two years of cadavers, post-mortems, etc., is depersonalization. Student repeatedly told by instructors to be "objective." Without humanizing warmth of patient as counterbalance, student runs risk of becoming impersonal, detached physician.

Re results of seven-year child rearing study, Spock and group finding answers to some old plaguing questions of early practice years.

Example 1: To answer the question, "How many mothers can't breast-feed babies at all?"

Answer: Any mother can breast-feed baby if she really wants to. There are a very few who don't have sufficient nourishment to meet baby's need.

Example 2: To answer the question, "Why are babies hard to wean from bottle to cup?"

Answer: Babies are not hard to wean from bottle to cup if baby is given bottle to hold in his hands while he is still in the crib-stage of development.

Example 3: To answer the question, "Why do bright young mothers, especially college graduates, find toilet training of babies their toughest problem?"

Answer: They are *all* afraid of arousing hostility in child. Are confused by so many opinions expressed by experts * in "baby books"—are afraid anything they do will be wrong, so better to do nothing!

"I wrote *Baby and Child Care* in the evenings from 1943 to 1946, when it was published simultaneously in hard cover and paperback editions. The aim was to cover the emotional as well as the physical aspects of child care, in a tone which

---

Spock, with characteristic candor, included himself among the experts whose diverse opinions have contributed to mothers' confusion.

would support rather than scold parents. It has sold sixteen million copies in eighteen years and been translated, probably inadvisably, into twenty-six languages. It was extensively revised in 1957, particularly in encouraging parents to give firm leadership to their children."

COMMENT

Spock calls himself a "developmentalist." Gets disturbed when he is referred to as a "permissivist." Explains that first edition of *Baby and Child Care* stressed flexibility as protest against rigidity of pediatric ideas and practice in early forties. For example, he encouraged "self-demand" feeding rather than rigidly timed feeding schedules.

In the first full revision of his book eleven years later, Spock says he shifted emphasis to parents' rights, need of direction, need to take leadership, etc.,—to counteract a "tidal wave of overpermissiveness." Thinks tidal wave began right after the turn of the century as a swing away from strict upbringing. Believes reasons partly protest against artificiality of Victorian era, partly because we are a pioneer society impatient with tradition. This is why he thinks we threw old mores, customs, religious patterns overboard when we were told "biology, psychology and sociology will give us all the answers." Now they tell us they don't know the answers either!

"I collaborated on two other books, *A Baby's First Year*, with John Reinhart and the photographer, Wayne Miller, and *Feeding Your Baby and Child*, with Miriam Lowenberg.

"From 1954 to 1963 I wrote monthly articles for *The Ladies' Home Journal* and these were the materials from which were made two books, *Dr. Spock Talks with Mothers*, 1961, and *Problems of Parents*, 1962, both published by Houghton Mifflin. Since 1963 I've written for *Redbook*. In recent years I've emphasized the necessity for relating child rearing to the needs of the nation and the world."

82

COMMENT

I asked Spock his views about today's teen-agers, whether he shared widespread adult disturbance over so-called "teen-age problem" and what about the notion that youth today are wilder and more irresponsible than our generation? In answer he said, "I don't view the young people of today with alarm because the majority of them are okay. In general, they are no worse than our generation and in some respects they are better. Certainly many of them are more aware of social problems than we were. Some of them are actually risking their lives to correct our wrongs. As to adults being disturbed, there is no question that they are. But I think the reason for the widespread disturbance is not that teenagers are worse today, but rather that parents today are confused and perplexed about the whole business of child rearing. In spite of good intentions, professionals in child development like ourselves have probably compounded parents' confusion by flooding them with indigestible doses of new and often divergent points of view about how to raise children."

In his book *Problems of Parents*, Dr. Spock has a final section called, "Critical Problems of Today and Tomorrow." Under a subheading entitled, "Will Our Children Meet the World Challenge?" he addresses himself more fully to the problem of parental confusion in America and gives what he believes are some of the reasons for the confusion.

America, in earlier generations, was excited, and unified to a degree, by the drives to push back the frontier, found a new nation, welcome pioneers and freedom seekers from all over Europe, create plenty for everyone by industrialization. In two world wars, there were prodigious feats of total mobilization in the cause of saving our country and preparing the way for a better world. But after each war the sense of high purpose gave way to preoccupation with individual and material concerns. . . .

Our diverse and individualistic aims, our lack of old traditions, would have made it difficult for us in any case to settle on a

83

philosophy of life which would give us all a firm sense of direction in rearing our children. But the problem has been enormously complicated by the flood of unsettling new concepts which came from the professions concerned with child development. (It is significant that European parents have been much slower to accept these ideas.)

Eager to bring up well-adjusted children according to the new theories but anxious about all the pitfalls, many of us have been hesitant and overpermissive. Our children have felt the lack of firm guidance and have acted up. We have been irritated by their behavior, of course. But instead of giving them more direction, we have felt guilty about our shortcomings and tried harder to be patient. These tangled feelings of ours are just the ones which will provoke children to rudeness, whining, squabbling, abuse of toys and furnishings. . . .

There are plenty of causes crying for America's concern. We urgently need more and better schools and universities, new housing, more adequate provisions for medical care, a solution for our racial discrimination. The poor underdeveloped countries of the world are begging for our technical, educational, medical and financial assistance. The communist nations which are out to beat us in every field of competition are gaining in productivity, giving more assistance to backward peoples, winning allies and friends faster than we.

We only need arouse ourselves, with the inspiration of bold leaders, and we'll have enough crusades to absorb us for decades. Then we might simultaneously find ourselves, save the world from destruction and give our children a new sense of dedication and worth.

In a recent speech, Dr. Spock made the point he was driving at in *Problems of Parents* even clearer by saying, "One fault of the twentieth century is that too many of us are too preoccupied with how to make our children secure. . . . We've thought too much on how we can do more for them

84

than how to prepare them to serve . . . and save the world."

It should come as no surprise to the reader that the man who believes children should be taught to serve is himself a front-line "server" in the cause of human rights. There are many men who share Dr. Spock's convictions but, unlike him, either through lack of courage or because they have succumbed to the tranquilizing effect of that old reliable bromide "discretion is the better part of valor," they are unable to speak when the moment of truth arrives.

Although Dr. Spock is a distinguished member of such professional societies as the American Academy of Pediatrics, the American Pediatric Society, the American Orthopsychiatric Association, the Group for the Advancement of Psychiatry and the Cleveland Academy of Medicine, he has never hesitated to take a stand on a controversial medical issue, even if it involves assuming a position directly opposed to that of organized medicine.

The final paragraph of *A Brief Autobiographical Sketch of Benjamin McLane Spock* shines with a luster of its own that no added comment of mine could possibly enhance. It is presented, therefore, without comment:

My pleasures are ice skating (dancing) in winter and cruising in a sailboat, up and down the New England coast, which I do all summer and dream about all the rest of the year.

WILLIAM MONTAGUE COBB

Pioneer in Anatomy and
Medical Anthropology

[1904–   ]

"Like men, I trow, to like God ever leads."
(Socrates in *Phaedrus*) *

In the idiom of the space age, the above maxim would probably come out of a computer compressed into "like men
model like." But whether phrased in Socratic dialogue or
clicked out in computer chatter, the underlying eternal verity
is the same, namely, men are forever drawn to those most
like themselves and, implicitly or explicitly, choose as models
the brightest stars within their own orbit. To learn, therefore, that Montague Cobb's chosen models include Vesalius,
Leonardo da Vinci, John Hunter, Thomas Wingate Todd
and the late Alexander Meiklejohn is to hold in one's palm
the key to his character.

William Montague Cobb was born in Washington, D.C.,
on October 12, 1904, the son of William Elmer and Alexzine

*Dialogues of Plato, *translated by J. Wright, M.A., A. L. Burt Co.,* Publishers, New York, 1950.

Montague (Cobb). He received his elementary education from two public schools—Patterson and Garnet—and completed his high-school education by graduating from Dunbar High School in 1921.

He attended Amherst College, where he majored in biology, won his varsity letter in track and cross country running and met his first living model, Alexander Meiklejohn, then the president of Amherst. By the time Cobb graduated from college in 1925, he had racked up two additional honors. In the academic realm, he won Amherst's coveted Blodgett Scholarship for proficiency in biology, which carried with it a year of study at the Marine Biological Laboratory, in Woods Hole, Massachusetts. In the athletic arena, he won championship boxing titles in two classes—lightweight and welterweight.

Cobb went to Howard University for his training in medicine. Here he took his M.D. degree in 1929 and completed a year's internship in 1930. He had every intention of going into practice as soon as he had finished his internship and passed his medical boards because, by this time, he had a wife, a child and no money! But fate, in the person of Dr. Numa P. G. Adams, dean of the Howard University Medical School, entered the picture at this point in his career. The result was that Cobb's future course was completely altered and recharted into a new channel. Instead of going into practice, he was persuaded by Dean Adams to accept a traveling scholarship from Howard, to spend two years at Western Reserve University, studying under Dr. Thomas Wingate Todd, distinguished professor of anatomy and director of the Hamann Museum of Comparative Anthropology and Anatomy of the School of Medicine.

Thomas Wingate Todd, like Alexander Meiklejohn, was

a Scotsman who never quite lost his "burr" during the twenty-six years he chaired the department of anatomy at Western Reserve. The son of a nonconformist, Wesleyan Methodist minister, Dr. Todd was an anatomist who built his laboratory in the "Hunterian" tradition. Like his illustrious English predecessor, John Hunter, Todd conceived of anatomy and physical anthropology not as static sciences, concerned only with graphic representations of human anatomical parts or their animal analogues, but as dynamic sciences, engaged in the study of anatomy as a basic biologic process in human development. By taking this position, both Hunter and Todd put themselves at odds with the teachings of the orthodox English school of anatomists.

All of which is relevant to the professional development of Montague Cobb because the course he chose to follow led him along the road charted by Hunter and Todd. It also led to his becoming, like his models, an independent and highly original investigator and, ultimately, the brilliant, dynamic teacher he is today.

With his Ph.D. from Western Reserve in his pocket, Cobb returned to Howard in 1932, as a full-time assistant professor of anatomy. In 1934, he became an associate professor and in 1942 attained the rank of full professor of anatomy. He was made head of the Department of Anatomy at Howard in 1947, a post he has continued to hold ever since.

William Cobb's studies in anatomy and physical anthropology have won him international recognition. His publications in the fields of anatomy, physical anthropology, dental morphology, medical history, medical education and public health now total some three hundred sixty-five, including five bound volumes. He is the author of the chapter on the "Skeleton" in the third revision of Cowdry's *Problems of Aging*, a standard

88

reference text. Two of his papers are cited in the current edition of Gray's *Anatomy*, known to medical students from time immemorial as the "Bible" of anatomy!

In the field of physical anthropology, Cobb's studies on the American Negro are considered by fellow anthropologists to be the most authoritative in this area. In addition to being scientifically sound, his research studies have provided documentation to refute the myths about the biological inferiority of the Negro. When *Life* magazine prepared a series of articles on the history of the American Negro, Cobb was chosen as consultant to the editor responsible for the series.

The esteem in which he is held by his fellow scientists is evidenced by the high offices they have elected him to fill. From 1949 to 1951 he served as president of the Anthropological Society of Washington. In 1958 he was elected to the presidency of the American Association of Physical Anthropologists for a two-year term. He is a vice president and currently a member of the Council of the American Association for the Advancement of Science. He has served as the official representative of the American Association of Anatomists to the Third Congress of the International Association of Gerontology in London and, a few years later, was named official representative of the American Association of Physical Anthropologists to the meeting of the International Association of Gerontology, held in Merano, Italy.

In addition to the offices he has held in associations of fellow anatomists and anthropologists, Dr. Cobb's breadth of knowledge and competence in other areas of medicine have led to his being tapped to serve on a wide variety of committees and boards. These have included membership on the Board of Directors of the American Heart Association, on the Board of Directors of the American Eugenics Society and on the Postdoctoral Fellowship Committee of the National Science Foundation-National Research Council Committee for the award of fellowships of the National Science Foundation and NATO. In each of these offices, he was the first of his race to be asked to serve.

He is a member of the Alpha Omega Alpha (honorary medical) and the Sigma Xi (honorary scientific) societies, as well as numerous scientific and professional societies.

Dr. Cobb's contributions to the basic medical sciences, together with his unique ability to combine scientific know-how with professional statesmanship, would have assured him a niche in the hall of medicine. But the talents of this extraordinarily gifted man extended far beyond the boundaries of these particular competencies. Like the greatest of his models, Leonardo da Vinci, he is a thirteenth-century-style, all-around "complete" man, for, in addition to being scientist, physician and medical statesman, he is a teacher, a musician, an artist and a medical historian. He is also a tireless fighter in the battle for human rights.

As a teacher, Cobb has had a hand in the education of over two thousand medical and fourteen hundred dental students who have graduated from Howard since he began his teaching career in 1932, as an assistant professor of anatomy. The basic tenet he has tried to get across to students over the years is that "anatomy is the one fundamental fact of biology." His method of teaching is based on the theory of reinforcement by repetition or, in his own words, "Drill, drill, drill until skill becomes automatic." * He believes that learning anatomy is like learning to drive a car or to box or to play a musical instrument. In all these skills, mastery is achieved through constant practice and repeated drill.

*Personal interview with the author, August, 1964.

Cobb's two hats as medical statesman and medical historian have been so interchangeable over the years that they can hardly be treated separately. Under the statesman's crown he served for six years as recording secretary and six years as president of the Medico-Chirurgical Society of the District of Columbia. During the same period of time, under the historian's crown, he wrote the history of the Society, collated all its records and preserved the total in permanent form.

That this overlapping of roles has continued up to the present time is evidenced by the fact that during all fourteen years when he has held the job as Editor of the *Journal* of the National Medical Association he has simultaneously served on such public bodies as: The Public Health Advisory Council of the District of Columbia, the District of Columbia General Vocational Rehabilitation Council, the United States Children's Bureau's, Advisory Committee on Maternal and Child Health and Crippled Children's Services and the Board of Trustees of the Junior Police and Citizens' Corps.

Today, the dual crowns consist of one new and one old. The new one is the presidency of the National Medical Association, an office to which he succeeded in August 1964. The old one, the editorship of the *Journal* of the National Medical Association, he continues to hold, but on leave of absence status, during his tenure as president of the Association.

Cobb's indentification with the last of his chosen models, Alexander Meiklejohn, is clearly visible in the field of human rights. The bond which united these two men continued from the moment they met, when Cobb entered Amherst College in 1921, until Meiklejohn's death on December 16, 1964.

As previously indicated, Alexander Meiklejohn was a Scotsman, born in England, who came to this country at the age of eight. Educated at Brown and Cornell, he began his academic career as an instructor in philosophy at Brown. He rose to become professor of logic and metaphysics at Brown and from this post moved to the presidency of Amherst in 1912. From the very beginning, it was clear that Meiklejohn was an educational innovator who had no intention of preserving the *status quo*. During his tenure as president, he reshaped the curriculum of Amherst College, with emphasis on the social sciences, and placed control of student activities in the hands of the students themselves, with a self-governing board.

Although Amherst flourished under these innovations, an internecine battle developed within the faculty which ultimately led to open warfare. In 1923, by a unanimous vote of the board, backed by a majority of the faculty, Alexander Meiklejohn was asked to resign the presidency he had held for twelve stormy years.

Many men who pay the price for defending unpopular beliefs seldom live to see the causes for which they fought win out or themselves vindicated. Meiklejohn was one of those rare exceptions who did. In later years, among the many other honors conferred on him were an honorary degree from Amherst College and the Presidential Medal of Freedom, presented to him in 1963 by President Kennedy, in recognition of his profound influence on American education.

Montague Cobb, in the manner of his friend and model, has fought with courage and vigor in the long battle for equal rights. As a scientist, he openly protested and refused to attend any scientific meetings that were held in segregated facilities. Out of regard for his professional and personal integrity, many colleagues of both races took the same position, with the result that scientific bodies like the American Association for the Advancement of Science and the American Association of Anatomists passed resolutions which barred meeting places that had segregated facilities. But Dr. Cobb's greatest reward came in the form of a letter he received from former Secretary of the Navy, the Honorable Francis P. Matthews. As one of twelve civilian guests of the Secretary on a cruise aboard the U.S.S. *Missouri* in 1950, Cobb observed incidents that seemed to indicate discriminatory policy on the part of the Navy. Through the good offices of Lieutenant Commander (then Lieutenant) Dennis D. Nelson, these were brought directly to the attention of the Secretary. Under the date of August 4, 1950, Secretary Matthews advised Dr. Cobb that,

It is the Navy policy that there shall be equality of treatment and opportunity in the Navy Marine Corps without regard to race, color, religion or national origin. In the utilization of housing, messing, berthing, and other facilities, no special or unusual provisions will be made for the accommodation of any minority race. I have further directed in the implementation of this policy that the Navy must not be a party to racial or partisan developments by incident or accident. The Navy will not officially participate in endorsing, sanctioning, promoting or subsidizing affairs of local sponsors in extending hospitality which involves or implies restriction, segregation or discrimination of racial or other groupings, at variance with the policies stated above.

Returning to the Leonardo-like diversity of talents theme brings us finally to the musician, artist and husband-father categories that, together with all the rest, constitute the "complete man," William Montague Cobb.

In the husband-father category, Cobb married Miss Hilda B. Smith, also a graduate of Howard University, in 1929. Mrs. Cobb, who majored in education, has continued to teach in Washington public schools ever since she got her degree from Howard. The Cobbs have two daughters, Carolyn Elizabeth (Mrs. Robert S. Wilkinson, Jr.), A.B., Mt. Holyoke, 1951; and Hilda Amelia (Mrs. Leander C. Gray), B.A., Carleton, 1960; M.F.A., Yale, 1963. There are three grandchildren—Amy, Karen and Robert Montague Wilkinson.

Cobb plays the violin and paints water colors for sheer enjoyment. He considers himself strictly an amateur in both media, even though he is a member of the Doctors' Symphonetta of Washington and has had his water colors exhibited in art shows devoted to paintings by doctors.

As a physician, anatomist, anthropologist and scientist, Montague Cobb has been familiar to me for many years—through his contribution to basic research, his publications covering a wide spectrum of medical and scientific knowledge, and his reputation as one of the fast-disappearing breed of physician-teachers that began with William Osler.

A whole series of interviews would have added nothing to my knowledge of Dr. Cobb in the areas of his professional competence. But if I had attempted to draw a sketch of him without meeting and talking with him, all the foregoing would have ended up in a compilation of statistics, for it is as a person that he comes alive, the brilliant composite of all his models. This is the person who, in the course of a three-hour interview which began in his office-laboratory at Howard with a discourse on anatomy and wound up in his home with the playing of a violin concerto, became the living composite of all his individual models.*

*Personal interview with the author in August, 1964.

94

ANNA FREUD

*Pioneer in Psychoanalysis and Child
Therapy*

[1895-   ]

To colleagues in adult psychiatry, she is a distinguished
psychoanalyst and child therapist; to child psychiatrists here
and abroad, she is the dean of child analysts; to those in the
trade, she is "the analyst's psychoanalyst"; to patients, she is a
therapist with a charismatic power of healing, but to children
she is none of these. To children she is an enchanting grownup
whose name is one word—"Annafreud!"

Anna Freud is the youngest of the six children—three boys
and three girls—of Sigmund and Martha (Bernays) Freud.
Except for a daughter who died of influenza during the widespread epidemic of 1919, Freud's other five children are living.
This daughter had a son who is now a psychoanalyst in London. The eldest son is a lawyer, the middle son is an engineer,
the third son is an architect, the other daughter was married
and is now a widow.

Anna Freud was born in Vienna, Austria, on December 3,
1895. Except for the few years when she attended the Cottage
Lyzeum, where she was graduated in 1912, she was privately
educated. Although she had attended no formal courses in

teacher training which the University provided in its curriculum, she took the examination for certification as a teacher and passed it with flying colors.

She began her career as an elementary-school teacher at the age of nineteen and for the next five years taught children in the early primary grades. This teaching experience gave her the background of understanding and knowledge of very young children that she later brought to bear in her analytic studies of child behavior and in the methods she developed for treating severely disturbed children.

At twenty-four, she went into psychoanalysis and, after spending the required number of years in psychoanalytic training, became a member and later, chairman, of the analytic institute in Vienna. This was the period during which she developed a method for adapting psychoanalytic techniques to the analysis of children. With the publication of *The Ego and the Mechanisms of Defense*, in 1937, she moved into the forefront of psychoanalysis in general. By 1938, when she left Austria to accompany her father to England, she had become Chairman of the Institute of Psychoanalysis in Vienna. She had also become the director of an experimental day nursery called the Jackson Nursery, which she organized in Vienna in 1937.

It was during and after the Second World War that Anna Freud made her contributions that were best known to the public in the field of psychoanalysis in general and, more specifically, in the area of research on childhood behavior disorders. Two of them, *Infants Without Families; the Case for and Against Residential Nurseries* * and *War and Children*,† are based on studies she and her colleague, Dorothy

*Infants Without Families; the Case for and Against Residential Nurseries, A. Freud and D. Burlingham, International Universities Press, Inc., New York, 1944.

†War and Children, A. Freud and D. Burlingham, Medical War Books, New York, 1943.

Burlingham, carried out in conjunction with the famous "Hampstead War Nurseries" program for children made homeless by the war.

This humanitarian service came about as a result of the joint efforts of two individuals and a voluntary agency, working in concert for the welfare of children. Anna Freud and Dorothy Burlingham operated the Hampstead Nursery in England, which was supported by the Foster Parents' Plan for War Children, Inc., New York, from 1940 to 1945. The core services consisted of residential facilities for about eighty children and a day nursery. The two residential units were Netherhall Gardens in London, with accommodations for about fifty children, from birth to five years of age, and "New Barn," Lindsell near Chelmsford, Essex, a country house for children evacuated from the London blitz. The day nursery on Wedderburn Road in London was run for the children from the residential nursery and some outside children. Attached to the service program of the Hampstead Nurseries was a three-year training course for children's nurses and teachers.

The general objectives of the Foster Parents' Plan for War Children, Inc., as well as the specific purposes of the War Nurseries are listed in the Foreword to *Infants Without Families* and in the Introduction to *War and Children*. The following quotations are excerpts selected from each:

The Hampstead Nursery is a Colony of the Foster Parents' Plan for War Children, Inc., New York, and as such owes its whole existence to American generosity. Like the other Colonies of the Foster Parents' Plan, it provides wartime homes for children whose family life has been broken up temporarily or permanently owing to war conditions. Like the other Colonies of the Foster Parents' Plan, although residential, it is not run on institutional lines. It tries to re-establish for the children what they have lost: the security of a stable home with its opportunities for individual development. The only characteristic of institutional life which it is powerless to avoid is the absence of the family itself.*

Work in War Nurseries is based on the idea that the care and education of young children should not take second place in wartime and should not be reduced to wartime level. It has already been generally recognized, and provision has been made accordingly, that the lack of essential foods, vitamins, etc., in early childhood will cause lasting malformation in later years, even if harmful consequences are not immediately apparent. It is not generally recognized that the same is true for the mental development of the child. Whenever certain essential needs are not fulfilled, lasting psychological malformations will be the consequence. These essential elements are: the need for personal attachment, for emotional stability, and for permanency of educational influence. . . . On the basis of these convictions our efforts are directed towards four main achievements:

To repair damage already caused by war conditions to the bodily and mental health of children. . . .

To prevent further harm being done to the children. . . .

To do research on the essential psychological needs of children. . . .

To instruct people interested in the forms of education based on psychological knowledge of the child; and generally to work out a pattern of nursery life which can serve as a model for peacetime education. . . .

An indication of how successful these two highly trained, dedicated women were in accomplishing their fourfold mission is contained in a preface to *War and Children* by the Executive Chairman of Foster Parents' Plan for War Children, Inc.

More than 20,000 cases of children have been studied by our staff members since our work began; at no time have we had any work

*Op. cit., *Foreword.*

98

to compare with the book *War and Children,* by Anna Freud and Dorothy Burlingham.

The Hampstead War Nurseries program came to a close with the end of the war, in 1945. For several years following the war, Anna Freud did not engage in any organized clinic work. Instead, she divided her time between treating child patients in private practice and continuing her work as an analyst, as well as teaching and supervising the young analysts in training.

This state of affairs might have continued indefinitely if it had not been for a few of her close friends and colleagues who felt she had a role to play on a larger stage. These were the people who, more than anyone outside her circle, were aware of the enormous contribution she had made to the war nurseries and who had long since recognized Anna Freud as one of those unique individuals who, in addition to having rare talents to begin with, had acquired a body of knowledge about children that was unmatched. Among her contemporaries she had a background that included teaching in elementary schools, organizing and directing an experimental nursery school, conducting teaching seminars on analysis for other analysts, and giving courses on child development to teachers, parents, physicians and nurses. And who but Anna Freud had published a book in 1937 called *The Ego and the Mechanisms of Defense* that is still considered the standard work on the theory of ego development by her colleagues both past and present?

So, at the continued urging of friends, Anna Freud planned and organized a treatment and training clinic at Hampstead, London, which opened in 1952. Since then, the Hampstead Child Therapy Course and Clinic has developed into a child center, unique in its class, where research, treatment and training in child development, child guidance and psychoanalysis are carried out in a combined program under one roof and a single director. The units comprising the treatment-training-research program include: a well baby clinic for toddlers and mothers, a nursery school for normal children ages three to five, a pre-nursery school for toddlers under three, a nursery school for blind children (directed by Dorothy Burlingham), a training department for child analysts and a treatment service able to carry some seventy disturbed or mentally ill children in treatment.

This multifaceted program of the Hampstead Clinic has, from the beginning, been largely financed by grants from two American Foundations, the Field Foundation and the Grant Foundation, plus other foundations. In recent years, additional financial support for the research program has been provided by a grant from the United States National Institute of Mental Health.

In making the award under the foreign grants program, the National Institute of Mental Health took into account the following facts: that expert consultants regard the Hampstead Center as a unique clinic operation in psychoanalysis, child development and child guidance which has had a marked impact on psychoanalytic centers and child guidance clinics in the United States; that Miss Freud and her group have made outstanding contributions to the literature in the fields of theoretical and applied research in child development, child analysis and education; and finally, that many of the people who now hold top research positions in clinics and centers throughout the United States have been trained by the Hampstead Clinic staff.*

*In recognition of her outstanding contributions, two American universities have awarded her honorary degrees. In 1950, Clark University, Worchester, Massachusetts, awarded her the degree of LL.D. (honoris causa)

In commenting on her role as director of the Hampstead Clinic, Anna Freud says her job is that of "administrator" of the Clinic. To her this means running a good clinic on as little money as possible. Since almost all financial support comes from American sources in the form of grants, she has to spend much of her time preparing grant applications and writing reports of findings to the granting agencies. When I made a wry remark to the effect that nowadays paperwork had become a "necessary evil," she responded by saying gently, "No, not evil—just the way of life nowadays." She went on to point out that psychoanalysis per se doesn't need grants but that running clinics and doing research does take money and she asked where would we be without grants, because there seems to be no other source of funds available to support this kind of work. So she is very grateful to the American foundations and the NIMH for their generous support and she regards the paperwork involved as part of her job as clinic administrator.

When I asked about future goals for the clinic, she said she would not want to add any more departments but, instead, would prefer to do the work they are now doing in depth. She clarified what she meant by "in depth" when she said she would like "to be able to pursue what one wants to do for children regardless of money."

The words in quotes in the preceding paragraph are some of the things Anna Freud said during an interview I had with her at the time of her most recent visit to the United States.* In preparation for the interview, I talked with colleagues, to learn something about her from their point of view, as to her characteristics, strengths, likes and dislikes, hobbies—all the

*and in 1964, Jefferson Medical College, Philadelphia, conferred on her the degree of Sc.D. (honoris causa).
Personal interview with the author—September 1964.

personal attributes that together constitute the essence, the quality, the style of an individual.

In the eyes of her colleagues, she has not only a superb intellect but also a charm of manner. She has graciousness, wit and serenity. Her simplicity, sincerity and integrity of character impress everyone who comes in contact with her. She is helpful but not a do-gooder. She is orderly in her work and has a high sense of duty.

Reason, good sense and hard work were given a high priority in the values of the Freud family. It was a household which was permeated also with a real joy of living. There was a deep curiosity about, and love of, nature. The family walking expeditions, led by Father, took in the rich variety of the landscape in all its aspects—its stones, trees, flowers, soil. Those expeditions that involved collecting mushrooms were especially exciting for two reasons, the obvious one being that mushrooms are a special treat, the less obvious being the satisfaction that goes with acquiring a new skill, in this case, expertise in the morphology and taxonomy of fungi. The fact that accuracy in differentiation between *agaricus campestris* and *amanita muscaria* is crucial to survival imbued the children with a profound respect for the interdependence of human beings with all other living things.

Even today, long walks in the country on weekends and in summer are not only a source of pleasure, they are a necessity to Anna Freud. During the summers, which she spends in her country house in Suffolk, she also rides horseback every morning. She goes swimming and boating when time and weather oblige.

Her time is not wasted on superficial social life because most of it is given to her work. There are too many people who need to be seen for professional or personal reasons. All

her services to the clinic as administrator, supervisor, co-
ordinator and research director are given gratis. She accepts
fees from private patients only. She is the soul and inspiration
of the clinic staff.

One other view of Anna Freud is needed to round out the
picture of her. As a teacher, she is acknowledged by everyone, from full professors to first year medical students, to
possess that rarest of teaching skills, the ability to translate
highly abstract theories and concepts into terms and words
that are clearly understood by everyone. Hers is the kind of
gift that, after hearing her lecture, you find yourself saying,
"But, of course, it seems as if I really *knew* that all along,
only why can't I ever say it that way!" Her rapport with an
audience, whether large or small, in public or in small groups,
is extraordinary.

The following excerpt from a lecture she gave a few years
ago at the University of California in Los Angeles is a particularly good example of her skill because it puts her concept
of ego development into words and terms that anyone can
understand.

"At the beginning of life we know that action is wholly in the
service of instinctual wishes but luckily, though the wishes are
strong at the beginning of life, action is very much restricted.
This begins to be a dangerous situation when the child grows,
becomes stronger, has independent movement, and when even
his actions carry him beyond the narrow circle of the family.
What is essential now for normality is that action should be under
ego control and not under the control of the id. This is most
painful for human beings because it causes such delay. It is as if
you had installed a special department in the city or in the university where you have to ask for permission first before you can
carry out any desirable action; you have to get approval. Just
think how quickly you could reach your aims if this were not

necessary, and still this is one of the most important safeguards of normality; that there is this type of civil service department, as we call it in England, installed in the personality itself within the ego which has to be consulted and also obeyed or rather the decision is to be waited for before appropriate action can be taken. This does not always happen, by any means.

You talk of impulsive people, the extreme end would be what one calls a crime of passion. This means that some urge, some aggressive wish was kept wholly from ego control, and the destructive urge satisfies itself regardless of consequences. Why this special delaying department has been built up is, of course, easy to see, and to the psychoanalytic students this is taught in the special courses on ego psychology." *

*"The Concept of Normality," *Medical Faculty Lecture, the University of California at Los Angeles, April 2, 1959.*

THE POLIO STORY

IN 1952, fifty-eight thousand children and adults in the United States came down with poliomyelitis and some three thousand of them died of the disease. By 1963, the number of polio cases for the entire year had dropped to a total of four hundred and thirty, the lowest number in a single year since reporting began in 1912!

The story of the conquest of this ancient scourge of mankind is one of the most stirring in the history of medicine. It is also one of the best examples of the changing face of medical research in the twentieth century, for the polio virus has been brought under control, not by the old familiar genius pottering among his test tubes in ivory tower isolation, but by small groups of highly skilled experts, working together for a common goal. Their research was supported largely by dimes and dollars contributed by the general public. The results of their scientific breakthrough were made available to the people through a skillfully organized program in which public health and medicine joined forces with unparalleled success.

Medical records from ancient times give evidence that poliomyelitis, or infantile paralysis, has existed for centuries. But it was not until the late nineteenth century that the incidence of polio reached epidemic proportions. At that time, North America, Scandinavia, Australia and New Zealand reported sizable numbers of cases.

In the United States, the first really widespread polio epidemic ever reported occurred in 1916, when there were 27,363 known cases, with 7179 deaths. These numbers represented 41.4 cases for every 100,000 people. For the next twenty-five years the number of diagnosed cases of polio remained at a level ranging from 2000 to 15,000 a year.

Then in 1943, the incidence of this disease took a sharp upswing and continued to increase until 1952, when it finally crested at a total of 58,000 cases.

These were the years when polio was the most dreaded disease of childhood and when fear reached panic proportions during the summer months, the peak season for polio epidemics. This was why, as summer approached, mothers experienced an increasing dread of swimming pools, summer camps, movie theaters, ball parks and all the places where close human contact with other children increased the risk of infection to their own.

Then came 1953, the year that ushered in the experimental trials of polio vaccine which paved the way for wholesale immunizations of the public carried out in 1954 and 1955.

Poliomyelitis as a national health threat has been conquered. The victory is a perfect example of modern, coordinated "building-block" research, where the final product—in this case, the production of polio vaccine—represents the keystone in the arch. The keystone could slip into place only after all the other blocks in the arch had been built up, one upon the other, by the combined effort of all concerned—the planners, the researchers, the manufacturers, the distributors, the health professionals, the volunteers, the educators, the legislators and the people. It is appropriate that the story of this concerted endeavor be represented graphically at Warm Springs, Georgia, in the Polio Hall of Fame. It was here that President Franklin D. Roosevelt came for treatment of paralysis that resulted from his attack of polio. It was also the base from which he launched the program of the National Foundation for Infantile Paralysis, founded by him in 1938. In the Hall of Fame in Warm Springs, there are busts of scientists whose work covered a time span of over a century, and of two lay-men who organized the fight against polio. The busts were unveiled on January 2, 1958, during ceremonies marking the twentieth anniversary of the National Foundation for Infantile Paralysis, parent organization of the March of Dimes, which has sponsored polio research since 1938.

These sixteen men and one woman and their contributions to the conquest of polio tell the story in brief:

Jacob von Heine—the first to describe polio clearly. He was the author of the first book on the disease, published at Stuttgart, Germany, in 1840.

Oskar Medin—a Swedish scientist who published a paper in 1890, in Stockholm, in which he was the first to recognize polio as an acute infection.

Ivar Wickman—a Swedish pioneer in the study of polio epidemics. In 1907, he commented on the wide prevalence of nonparalytic polio.

Karl Landsteiner—a Viennese physician who demonstrated that polio can be transmitted to an experimental animal, the monkey. He published a paper on the subject in 1909.

John R. Paul—a Yale University virologist who conducted the first virus research under a grant from the National Foundation, in 1938. He contributed to the knowledge of how polio is spread.

Charles Armstrong—Public Health Service physician who discovered in 1939 that certain strains of polio virus could be transmitted to cotton rats, thus simplifying certain types of later study.

Joseph L. Melnick—Yale University scientist, who helped to show how immunity developed in populations exposed to the polio virus.

Isabel Morgan—a Johns Hopkins University scientist, who prepared an experimental vaccine from virus inactivated with formaldehyde that protected monkeys against paralytic polio.

Howard A. Howe—another Johns Hopkins University scientist, and the first to show that chimpanzees can contact polio by mouth. He conducted small-scale experiments with humans, using a formalin-treated vaccine.

David Bodian—again, a scientist from Johns Hopkins, who demonstrated that the polio virus gets into the blood stream before reaching the central nervous system, and therefore could be blocked by antibodies in the blood.

John F. Enders—a scientist at the Children's Medical Center, Boston, who pioneered in growing polio viruses in cultures of nonnervous tissue, which opened the way for a safe and effective vaccine that could be mass-produced. He and his co-workers won the 1954 Nobel Prize in Medicine and Physiology.

Jonas E. Salk—a University of Pittsburgh scientist who developed the vaccine which bears his name. It was the Salk vaccine that accounted for most of the gain so far achieved in the dramatic lowering of the incidence of polio in the United States.

Albert B. Sabin—a Cincinnati University scientist and leader in the successful search for a live polio virus vaccine. His research helped show how the virus reaches the central nervous system. Distribution of the Sabin vaccine is increasing.

Thomas M. Rivers—Dean of American virologists, who was chairman of the National Foundation committee which planned the successful 1954 Salk vaccine field trials.

Thomas Francis, Jr.—a University of Michigan epidemiologist, who directed the 1954–55 evaluation program demonstrating the safety and effectiveness of the Salk vaccine.

Franklin Delano Roosevelt—thirty-second President of the United States, severely disabled by paralytic polio, who founded the Georgia Warm Springs Foundation in 1927 and the National Foundation for Infantile Paralysis in 1938, and inspired those who ultimately achieved the victory over the disease.

Basil O'Connor—a New York lawyer, leader in the fight against polio, president of the National Foundation since its formation, and of the Georgia Warm Springs Foundation since 1945.

The cost of success was high—neary $940,000,000 in research and other expenditures. But it is estimated that this nation would have spent over $9,000,000,000 in medical costs and in numerous other ways if polio had not been brought under control when it was.

Public fear of polio began with the 1916 epidemic in the United States. As one writer has stated, "This was the beginning of annual dread." It took one man, Franklin D. Roosevelt, to focus the attention of the world on this crippling disease and to inspire the greatest mass cooperative undertaking against a single health menace the world has ever known. He was striken by polio in 1921, and although he never walked again without the aid of leg braces, a cane and an assistant, he became President of the United States, elected to that office four times. His primary purpose in creating the

National Foundation (originally for Infantile Paralysis) was to provide leadership, direction and unity in the attack on polio.

The first step was to correlate and organize the already known facts about infantile paralysis or polio. Scientists had identified polio as an epidemic disease that affected more children than adults. They knew that a child who had recovered from polio was apt to be immune in the future. It was also known to be caused by a virus. A virus is far smaller than an ordinary germ, and is more difficult to control. Viruses, because of their ability to invade living body cells, can damage or destroy nerve cells. If enough nerve cells are affected, the result is paralysis or death.

Scientists did not know how the virus entered the body nor where it came from. There were conflicting theories which further clouded the picture. Sanitary measures seemed to produce no results—in fact, the opposite appeared to be true. In 1938, the questions about polio far outweighed the answers.

Literally millions of children and adults contributed to the annual March of Dimes. There were benefit balls on President Roosevelt's birthday, and on store counters hundreds of thousands of containers for dimes kept filling up throughout the year. All the money went into the National Foundation to support the scientific effort to eradicate polio. The resulting teamwork between the public and the world of science was wholly unprecedented.

With these funds, scientists and physicians were trained in the special techniques required for polio research; laboratories equipped for the specialized work were opened in several areas; and expensive monkeys were imported from Asia. In order to have enough healthy monkeys to work with, a monkey farm was established at Hardeeville, South Carolina, where these animals received the finest of care so that polio research could proceed without the added complications of other diseases to which monkeys are susceptible.

But when and where and how did research on polio actually begin? Back in 1909, Dr. Landsteiner had discovered the fact that polio could be transmitted to monkeys, and it was known that the virus multiplied in the spinal cord and brain of infected monkeys. But although this knowledge contributed to later findings, it created problems for modern researchers seeking to find a less expensive and more manageable way of growing the virus in quantity.

Then Dr. Armstrong, of the United States Public Health Service, found in 1939 that certain strains of polio virus could be transmitted to cotton rats, more easily obtainable and less costly than monkeys.

Drs. Paul and Melnick of Yale, along with Dr. Armstrong, also carried out studies on how polio spreads and how immunity develops in those exposed. It is now known that the polio virus can infect many thousands of persons, with only a small minority of those infected showing signs of the disease. Dr. John Fox made a detailed study of one hundred and fifty families in New Orleans and found that two hundred and forty persons in these families had developed antibodies that were not present at the start of the investigation. This means that they had been infected but had thrown off the disease without showing any symptoms or effects of polio.

About this time, research began to turn up evidence that polio was not just one strain of virus, but several, and recovery from one strain might not protect the individual from the other strains. Researchers then set about to determine how many kinds of polio virus there were.

Four university laboratories—Southern California, Utah, Kansas and Pittsburgh—using large research teams working on approximately twenty thousand monkeys, labored for three years testing one hundred strains of virus collected from all over the world. The cost was well over one million dollars in March of Dimes funds. But they found the answer: All known polio viruses could be classified into three types, now called Type I, Type II and Type III. So, a vaccine, to be effective, would have to protect against all three strains.

In 1949 there came a further major breakthrough. Three years before, Dr. John F. Enders had been appointed chief of research of the division of infectious diseases at the Children's Medical Center in Boston. A Ph.D. in microbiology from Harvard, and later associate professor of bacteriology and immunology at that university, Dr. Enders focused on experiments growing polio virus in tissue culture cells that would not be dangerous if the virus were used in a vaccine.

Dr. Enders and two associates from the Harvard Medical School, Dr. Thomas H. Weller and Dr. Frederick C. Robbins, discovered that they could grow polio virus on non-nervous tissue in a test tube. For this and related achievements, the three won the Nobel Prize in 1954.

There was now a practical means for growing virus inexpensively enough to use in vaccines, and hundreds of preliminary studies could be carried out simultaneously, with the virus growing in test tubes instead of in animals.

This discovery made possible the present-day methods for mass-producing the polio virus needed for the manufacture of vaccines. Another result was the development of many laboratory tests for polio in which a few test tubes of tissue culture can replace the previously used and costly live monkeys.

The next important building stone was added to the growing arch of polio knowledge when it was proved in 1952 that polio virus enters the bloodstream for a time before it attacks the nerve cells. To scientists, this meant that, if a sufficient number of antibodies were present in the blood, they could combat the polio virus before it could destroy nerve cells and cause paralysis. The two people most directly responsible for this discovery are Dr. Dorothy Horstmann of Yale University and Dr. David Bodian of the Johns Hopkins Medical School.

Dorothy Millicent Horstmann was born in Spokane, Washington. She attended the University of California, where she got her A.B. in 1936 and her M.D. in 1940. She began her career in the school of Medicine at Yale in 1942, as a Commonwealth Fund fellow. In 1943, she was appointed as instructor in preventive medicine at Yale, and thereafter rose to become an assistant professor, an associate professor and finally, in 1961, Professor of Epidemiology and Pediatrics, her present post.

A graduate of the University of Chicago, with honors in zoology, Dr. David Bodian received his Ph.D. from the University in 1934 and his M.D. in 1937, at the same time teaching microscopic anatomy, neuroanatomy and advanced neurology. After a year as a National Research Council fellow, studying neurology at the University of Michigan, he went to Johns Hopkins as a research fellow and began the teamwork there on polio. He is now director of the department of anatomy at Johns Hopkins.

These three discoveries of science—the growing of virus in a test tube on nonnervous tissue, the determination of three types of polio, and the proof that the virus enters the bloodstream for a time—held great meaning for a young scientist at the University of Pittsburgh, Dr. Jonas E. Salk. He applied for and received funds from the March of Dimes for a project to develop a vaccine.

Born in 1914, Dr. Salk published his first scientific paper while a student working extra hours in the chemistry laboratory at New York University College of Medicine. He spent nine months in the department of bacteriology at the University before serving his internship at Mt. Sinai Hospital, New York City.

In 1942, he went to the University of Michigan under a fellowship, to study with Dr. Thomas Francis, Jr., who later was to figure in the polio story also. He then went to the University of Pittsburgh, as director of its virus research laboratory, and in 1954 he became the chairman of the Department of Preventive Medicine.

He is now president and director of the Salk Institute of Biological Studies, San Diego, California.

Dr. Salk had directed the Pittsburgh team taking part in the polio-typing experiment, so he was well versed in his subject. The Salk vaccine did not spring full-blown from the laboratory. It was the result of innumerable experiments with vaccines, repeated tests and calculations and a continuous process of refining techniques. The production of vaccine is a vastly complicated process which begins with minced monkey tissue, goes through a series of painstaking laboratory procedures and repeated tests for safety, potency, and efficiency, until it is finally considered ready for human use. Each single dose of vaccine contains approximately a hundred million dead viruses.

The killed viruses still retain enough potency to step up

the antibody mechanisms in the bloodstream, thus giving protection against the invasion of live viruses. Experimental work on killed viruses and their inactivation by formaldehyde had been effectively performed at Johns Hopkins by Dr. Isabel Morgan and Dr. Howard Howe, who had also shown that chimpanzees could acquire polio by mouth. All these factors contributed to the success of the final product.

Dr. Howard A. Howe, who worked with Dr. Bodian, received his medical degree from Johns Hopkins in 1929. Born in Wabash, Indiana, he was appointed instructor in anatomy at the Johns Hopkins Medical School in 1930, and went on to become associate in 1940. When the Poliomyelitis Research Center was organized in the School of Public Health in 1943, he was made a staff member as an associate professor of epidemiology. In 1946, he was made adjunct professor in epidemiology. At the present time he holds the rank of adjunct professor, emeritus.

Dr. Isabel Morgan is the daughter of T. H. Morgan, Nobel Prize winner for his theory of genes in 1933. She attended Stanford University and Cornell University and earned her Ph.D. in bacteriology at the University of Pennsylvania. Immediately upon graduation, she joined the Rockefeller Institute, to do research on the encephalitis viruses. She and her colleagues were responsible for isolating a strain of polio virus derived from a British soldier who had died from the disease at El Alamein. In 1944, she joined the Hopkins polio team.

After innumerable tests of the Salk vaccine, field trials began. They were done in three parts: (1) vaccination of a sufficient number of children and the establishment of suitable control groups of unvaccinated children; (2) collection of information on all of these children, both before and after

FAMOUS MODERN MEN OF MEDICINE

the vaccination period, and through the polio season, with special information on children in the study group who developed polio; (3) analysis of all information received.

The first part of the vaccination trials (consisting of three shots) was completed in July 1954; the second by December 31, 1954; the third by April 12, 1955.

The vaccinations were given in clinics, schools, churches and public buildings, and were a stupendous undertaking. Twenty thousand physicians and health officials, forty thousand registered nurses, fourteen thousand school principals and fifty thousand teachers served as volunteers, as did two hundred thousand other citizens. Nearly two million children were involved in the vaccine trials. Pharmaceutical manufacturers cooperated in producing the vaccine.

Every detailed piece of information on each child went to the Polio Evaluation Center directed by Dr. Francis, at the University of Michigan. Altogether some one hundred and forty million separate pieces of information were collated and analyzed.

There were twenty-seven laboratories across the country working on the evaluation—checking blood samples of children who had participated, determining antibody levels before and after vaccination, and investigating numerous other factors to determine the success or failure of the vaccine.

On April 12, 1955, two hundred writers representing newspapers, radio, TV and magazines invaded Ann Arbor, Michigan, to hear Dr. Francis' report, and send the news out to a waiting world. With them were over five hundred scientists and health leaders, equally anxious.

Out of the carefully worded report, presented to the group by Dr. Francis in person, it soon became clear that the vaccine had worked. Pandemonium broke loose as the reporters scrambled out of the meeting room, each one trying to be the first to break the momentous news.

In the initial historic year following the field trials, the incidence of polio dropped from forty thousand to twenty-nine thousand cases. The next year, it was down to fifteen thousand. From that time, the incidence has decreased steadily with each year, until there were only some four hundred and thirty cases in the United States in 1963.

But still another major advance had been made between the discovery of Salk vaccine and the low incidence of 1963.

It came as a result of twenty-five years devoted to polio research by a physician who had emigrated to the United States with his parents from Bialystok, Russia. After financing much of his own education, Albert B. Sabin received his M.D. from New York University in 1931. He interned at Bellevue Hospital, in New York City, where his interest in polio research developed. He joined the research staff of the Rockefeller Institute to do research on polio viruses. Three years later he moved to the University of Cincinnati's College of Medicine, as associate professor of pediatrics, all the while increasing his knowledge and discoveries about polio.

He succeeded finally in isolating a live but harmless strain of polio virus which could be fed by mouth. Again, after exhaustive tests in the laboratory, first with animals and then with humans, the Sabin vaccine was found to be safe and highly effective in preventing polio.

The Sabin vaccine, containing all three types of virus, is given in three oral doses. By the end of 1963, the Sabin vaccine had been taken by some eighty million people in the United States, mainly through participation in large, community-wide vaccination programs.

Since 1959, distribution of the Salk vaccine has decreased,

while health authorities are turning more and more to the Sabin variety. Some of the reasons advanced for the increased use of the latter are: it is easier to administer than the Salk vaccine because it is given by mouth; it confers longer immunity; it is faster-acting, and it prevents the growth of wild polio viruses in the intestinal tract and their possible spread into the community.

And so, thanks to "building block research," with Salk and Sabin supplying the keystone of the arch, and due to the financial support of millions of American dimes and dollars, one of the ancient scourges of man has been conquered by men.

THE SURGERY STORY

LESS than a hundred years ago there were many surgeons who felt they had gone as far as possible into the human body and there were no new areas to conquer.

The twentieth-century surgeon, equipped with knowledge, technical aids and scientific gear undreamed of a generation ago, knows that he, like the space scientist, is only at the beginning of the age of discovery.

Recently, a patient who was dying of a kidney disease was given two extra months of life after receiving an ape kidney transplant. The case is far different from the old saying that the operation was a success but the patient died. The fact that the ape kidney functioned for two months in a human being is highly significant. The advisability of the operation is still being debated. Animal-to-man transplants may be the answer to the problem of organ failure in man, or they could be the clue to the right answer, which must come through trial and error.

"We may be making monkeys of ourselves," says one expert in transplants. But there is no doubt that we are making progress. There have already been many human kidney transplants, one of which extended a life eight years. Today's surgeon can replace a defective length of artery with knitted dacron; he can look deep into the body cavities with the aid of electronics, X-rays, ultrasonic rays, and other devices; he can plug a patient into a heart-lung machine that takes over the function of these vital organs during an operation; he can insert a stainless steel valve in the heart to replace a defective one. He can do all these things and many more, not just because surgical skill has increased (although it has), but mainly because other scientific advances are at his disposal. The surgeon no longer works alone; he is now part of a team. And the team is not only physician, surgeon, anesthetist, pathologist, radiologist, physiologist, biochemist, nurse, often psychiatrist and a variety of other specialists—but it includes nonmedical specialists like engineers, electronics experts, biologists, physicists, chemists and researchers in innumerable fields.

The surgeon of the twentieth century is the professional descendant of a long, and sometimes strange, line of ancestors. In the days of Hippocrates, three hundred years before Christ, surgery was performed with skill by physicians with a very limited knowledge of anatomy and disease. By the Middle Ages, however, the surgeon's knife had passed into the hands of barbers, sow-gelders and itinerant "specialists." It was not until the late nineteenth century that surgery could be respected as a science and an art as well—and even then the number of experts was small.

As more and more about the human body became known, the trend was toward specialization, until various parts of the anatomy came to be considered as separate entities, and there was little concern for the person as a whole human being whose entire body and mind were made to function in ordered harmony.

Next came subspecialization—one neurosurgeon became an expert in removing brain tumors, while another neurosurgeon concentrated on brain surgery to alleviate epileptic seizures.

By the time a specialty within a specialty had developed into such a fine art, the medical profession had learned a great deal about the whole person. We know now that not only are body functions interrelated, but that the patient is a whole person whose mind, body and emotions interact and affect each other. Hence, the team is a necessity, backed up and supported by modern scientific and technical aids which were not dreamed of a generation ago.

The two institutions which deserve the most credit for focusing attention on the whole person and not just a combination of symptoms are the Johns Hopkins University Medical School and Hospital, and the Mayo Clinic, both started in the late 1880's.

The Mayo Clinic, in Rochester, Minnesota, still holds to the rule laid down by its founders, three surgeons, William Worrall Mayo and his sons, William James and Charles Horace Mayo: * No patient is touched by a knife until every part of his body is examined thoroughly by a team of experts in various fields of medicine.

Baltimore's Johns Hopkins revolutionized medical education, mainly through the brilliant and courageous ideas of the four young men who set the pace for modern surgery and medical practice. They were William Osler, physician-in-chief; William H. Welch, pathologist; Howard A. Kelly, gynecologist and obstetrician; and William S. Halsted, surgeon.† Their most respected textbook was the patient himself, and the lectures at the university supplemented but never replaced their bedside observations.

Within twenty years after the first class was graduated from Johns Hopkins, over sixty American colleges or uni-

*See this volume, p. 40.
†Chandler, Caroline A.: Famous Men of Medicine, Dodd, Mead and Company, 1950, p. 90.

versities had three or more Hopkins graduates as professors on their staffs. Many of the most daring surgical operations now being performed throughout the world are the direct result of bold new approaches and techniques pioneered at Johns Hopkins by William Halsted, Harvey Cushing and other Hopkins greats.

Dr. Halsted's operations on hernia, breast cancer and thyroid are considered classics in surgery. He was capable of performing almost any operation—in fact, he successfully operated on his own mother for impacted gallstones, although he had never done this type of operation before and other specialists had strongly advised against it. But his greatest impact on surgery has come through the surgeons who trained under him. His inspiration and ability changed the course of surgery in the United States and in many parts of the entire world.

Neurosurgery, dealing with the nervous system, came of age at Johns Hopkins under the cool, scientific mind and steady hands of Harvey Cushing, the first real specialist in neurosurgery.*

In all surgery, success or failure is often determined by the path of the surgeon's instruments or fingers. Attack from the rear, the side, front, above or below can make the difference between life and death. But in brain surgery the results of error are sometimes more frightful than death. One slip in the wrong direction can deprive a man of his reason or his sight or memory or emotions—or even his moral values. The immediate risks in brain surgery are excessive bleeding and infection, once the protective membrane—the dura mater—is cut. The clamps and sutures used in other areas of the body to stop bleeding are too gross for the delicate structure of

*Chandler, Caroline A.: Famous Men of Medicine, Dodd, Mead and Company, 1950, pp. 109–113.

the brain. Cushing succeeded in controlling hemorrhage by the use of fine silver wire and little pieces of muscle. These surgical innovations freed him to enter previously forbidden areas.

Cushing also introduced into neurosurgery the use of electrosurgery, a technique which had recently been developed. The "knife" is an electric needle capable of the most delicate and selective exploration. Its added ability to coagulate blood makes it a highly refined modern version of the burning iron used in the Middle Ages to seal off bleeding points. It is now used as a cauterizer in other parts of the body as well as the brain.

An almost insurmountable difficulty for centuries was the localizing of functions and disorders within the brain. By experimenting with electrical stimulation, researchers mapped out the brains of animals, charting the function of each area. The only trouble with this system was that human brains do not correspond with animal brains in some respects, but it took thirty years or so for neurosurgeons to discover this discrepancy.

An idea of Dr. Halsted's was indirectly responsible for a tremendous advance in locating brain tumors. He had been impressed with the way in which gas showed up in X-rays of the intestines. He kept writing of this phenomenon and discussing it. Another Hopkins neurosurgeon, Walter Dandy, who had been house surgeon under Dr. Cushing, applied Halsted's idea to brain X-rays. Dr. Dandy injected air into the spaces of the brain and then took X-ray pictures of the skull. He found, as he had hoped, that alterations in the brain's shape due to a growth showed on the picture.

Some time later, the pattern of blood vessels in the brain was made visible by injection of a radio-opaque fluid.

At this period in the history of surgery, it was becoming

apparent that the surgeon no longer had to rely solely on his own diagnostic or operating skills. For diagnosis, operating aids and postoperative treatment, he was depending more and more on discoveries in the field of physics, engineering, electronics, and other sciences, as well as medicine.

At this point it is appropriate to take a look at some of the vast contributions other sciences have made to surgery within the last generation.

The use of X-rays is, of course, an old story, but new applications and refinements of this technique turn up every day. The fluoroscope is one adaptation of the "look-see" use of X-ray, in which parts of the body can be seen through the absorption of radiation.

Electronics has made possible not only the electrosurgery mentioned earlier, but also such innovations as the electrocardiograph machine (with which the heart rhythm can be charted), the encephalograph machine (which measures brain waves), and electroshock treatments for serious heart and brain disorders. The operating table of today is surrounded by innumerable electronic devices recording pulse, respiration, blood pressure, while others power life-saving devices like the heart-lung machine, among others.

The use of temperature control is a recent step in surgery. Surgeons are experimenting with reducing the body temperature during an operation to about 28 degrees centigrade for a short period, to slow down body mechanisms and allow more time for an operation. This procedure, called hypothermia, prevents the damage previously encountered when certain organs were without blood circulation for more than a very few minutes.

An even later development in thermal technique is cryosurgery, in which tissues are frozen and destroyed. Freezing needles at minus 40 degrees centigrade are inserted to destroy, or make inert, malignant tissue. Freon was the first gas used; now nitrogen is being used experimentally.

Medicine has just begun to apply the infinite uses of the computer in diagnosis and treatment. The surgeon can feed into a computer the patient's symptoms and all other pertinent information (age, overall health, environment, etc.) and receive a diagnosis. Or he can even get advice on whether, under the circumstances, it is feasible to operate. Computers can chart and compare results of tests on one patient or a number of patients, and quickly give out information it would take human beings days or weeks or even years to produce.

The use of television in today's surgery is not limited to Ben Casey, by any means. Television is a great teaching device for surgeons in particular. An operation previously seen by perhaps two dozen medical students some distance removed can now be observed at close range by thousands on closed-circuit TV.

In the same electronics field there is another of the latest aids to modern surgery—ultrasound. This technique makes use of ultra-high frequency sound waves, employing the principles of sonar, which locates underwater objects. Using sound waves, the surgeon can measure distances between the skull walls and the center of the brain, to determine whether the brain has been pushed to one side, as it would be by a cerebral hemorrhage or tumor. This type A-scan ultrasound is also capable of locating internal bleeding after brain surgery, gallstones, kidney stones, or any foreign object anywhere in the body.

Eventually, it may aid surgeons in spotting enlarged hearts, defective valves and other heart disorders through "echocardiograms."

Ultrasound has been adapted for direct use in surgery, to a limited extent. A tiny device that sends out a beam of ultrasound is mounted between the prongs of forceps that resemble small tweezers. The surgeon uses the forceps to locate and then remove foreign objects that have become lodged in the body—even in the delicate area of the eye. As the surgeon probes gently with the device, he tracks the progress on a screen that registers the echo from the sound waves and locates the object.

Of course, with the increasing number of "foreign objects" purposely introduced into the body by surgeons today, the ultrasound devices could go wild scanning the man of the future who may be held together with steel plates, wires, nails, catgut, nylon, dacron and enough materials to stock a small hardware-drygoods store!

But although modern surgery is an integrated science which makes use of other scientific advances so that the most delicate operations can be performed, no apparatus or device can take the place of the physician. It is his judicious use of machines which makes the machines important. It is his application of spare parts to anatomy which makes them work. The one part that can never be spared is the physician's human mind and heart in the treatment of human beings.

Spare parts to aid healing and prolong life have been used for over a hundred years, as surgeons have experimented—often successfully—with a wide variety of materials to hold together bones that had not knit properly, or to join a length of intestine that had been cut, or to contain brain matter within a damaged skull. One such foreign object that was used for a number of years was the Murphy button, which resembled a yo-yo with a hollow center spindle, and was placed in the gut after a certain type of abdominal operation.

Metals are used primarily for the treatment of difficult fractures and in reconstructing diseased joints. An outstanding man in this field is Marius Nygaard Smith-Peterson, a Boston orthopedic surgeon. He has developed a special nail with fins to strengthen the femur in the thigh after a fracture, a vitallium metal cup that fits over the hip joint, among other innovations. These metals are placed in the body after careful preparation with X-rays to control the body's natural mechanism to reject them.

There are still problems that arise from metals in the body. Occasionally they work loose, or they may corrode or present other problems that surgeons are now investigating.

Plastics offer more promise than metals. Plastics used by surgeons remain relatively inert within the body, especially those in the acrylic group. There is as yet no perfect material that is absolutely compatible with the body's mechanisms.

The Duke of Windsor, the former King of England, now is wearing a knitted dacron patch on an artery which had developed an aneurysm, or a bulge which is fatal if it bursts. The operation was performed by Michael Ellis DeBakey, head of Baylor University's department of surgery in Houston, Texas, the top man in the field of cardiovascular surgery, and inventor of the knitted dacron graft. He has performed over sixty-five hundred major cardiovascular procedures in the past six years, with a 95 per cent recovery rate.

Dr. DeBakey has patched damaged hearts, replaced heart valves that had stopped working, inserted miniature timing devices as pacemakers in the heart, substituted sections of arteries, and even tried a replacement for the whole left side of the heart, in each case using synthetics or metal. Sometimes, as in the artificial heart valve, DeBakey uses a combination. The valve consists of a stainless steel cage mounted on a ring with sharp teeth, and a hard plastic ball.

The operation replacing heart parts is one of the most delicate in modern surgery. It would be completely impossible without the aid of the heart-lung machine which takes over the work of the heart and lungs as it takes in dark, unoxygenated blood from the venae cavae, supplies it with oxygen, then pumps it through the femoral artery in the thigh.

Once the heart resumes functioning on its own, after the new valve has been attached and the heart-lung machine disconnected, there is danger that the heart may begin fibrillating or beating erratically. At this time the surgeon has recourse to another lifesaver of twentieth-century science, electrical stimulation, which pours over one thousand volts of electrical current into the heart and literally shocks it into proper rhythm.

An even more radical field of surgery that would have been called "humbug" a short time ago is the rebuilding of the human body through transplants of living organs. One of the major obstacles is the body's effort to reject the intruder.

Modern science is on the way to conquering this natural rejection mechanism, however, and today there is hope for "secondhand" kidneys, lungs, and other organs—perhaps even new hearts for old.

To lower the resistance and make the body more receptive to transplants, medical men have tried various types of conditioning. In one, the whole body is irradiated in so-called "sublethal" doses, and the patient is kept in an aseptic (germ-free) environment for a period of time. Another approach is a mixture of irradiation and drugs to suppress resistance. Drugs (chemotherapy) can be used exclusively, or radiation alone can be focused on either lymphoid tissues or the area to receive the transplant.

The combination of drugs and sharply focused irradiation before and after the operation is preferred by many physicians. The renowned authority on transplants, Dr. Michael Woodward, professor of surgery at the University of Edinburgh, feels that both are necessary, explaining that "irradiation lends itself to direction in space, and chemotherapy to control in time."

There are still no standards as to when to begin treatment, what the dosage should be and when it should stop—if ever. An added danger is that the drugs lower resistance to all disease and the patient is vulnerable to any germ, bacteria or virus that comes along. After the operation, too much chemotherapy may lead to infection, while not enough may invite rejection. The amount and time also vary with different patients.

The first two to four weeks after the transplant are crucial. If the body tolerates the foreign tissue by the end of about four weeks, chance of survival, limited though it may be at present, increases to a marked degree.

In early 1965, it was reported that about thirty persons have lived a year or more with a donated kidney, called a renal transplant. Although the time may seem short, one year added to a life that would have ended without the surgery is a step on the road to progress and proves that a transplant is feasible. Eventually, it is hoped that a person with a renal transplant can expect to live out his life span. The fact that it works at all is the crucial point.

Boston's Peter Bent Brigham Hospital has led the way in organ transplants and spare parts surgery. In 1954, a patient was dying of severe kidney failure when it was found that he had an identical twin. The surgeon, Dr. J. Harrison Hartwell, removed a kidney from the healthy twin and Dr. Joseph Murray implanted it in the ill twin. The patient lived for more than eight years. He died of a heart attack, but the kidney was still functioning at the time of death.

The best transplants come from identical twins who have the same body chemistry. Second-best donor is the mother. In the case of kidneys, nature has provided two, but it is possible to live a normal life with just one—as far as experience has proven to date.

George J. Macgovern and A. J. Yates of the University of Pittsburgh recently performed a human lung transplant on a patient dying of emphysema. One of the factors contributing to the relative success of the operation was the fact that the surgeons had been able to secure a healthy lung immediately from the body of a man in the same hospital who had just died of a circulatory disorder. He had been treated by hypothermia, the technique which considerably lowers the temperature and slows down all body functions. The lung, plus most of the pulmonary artery, was removed from the corpse, placed in a solution, then packed in ice and rushed down six floors to the operating room, where it was implanted in the living patient. It had been approximately one hour since the donor's lung had been removed, but once "connected" to the necessary body mechanisms and inflated, the lung immediately began to work. Although the patient died eight days later, the lung had functioned for that length of time, proving that the operation is potentially worthwhile and, with further experience, may offer new hope to those suffering from the terminal stages of emphysema.

Because it is difficult to secure organs from human beings, alive or dead, surgeons have been experimenting with animal organ grafts. The step is taken only when there is no other hope and the disease is in its last stages.

Dr. Claude Hitchcock, of Minneapolis, performed the first

ape-to-man operation in 1963, transplanting a kidney. At Tulane University's Medical School, Dr. Keith Reemtsma did two such heterogeneous transplants, with the second patient living two months following the operation. The other two died. In the patient who survived for two months, the organ began to work immediately after it was implanted. However, on the fourth day he showed symptoms of rejection (rise in temperature and other symptoms). The drug therapy which had been started a week before surgery was increased and the graft area was irradiated. Indications of rejection subsided and subsequent tests showed normal activity in the grafted kidney. The case is significant because it seems to be the first time physicians have been able to reverse the rejection mechanism, once it starts.

One surgeon went so far as to transplant a heart from a chimpanzee into a patient dying of heart disease. The heart beat one hour, then stopped.

There have been at least six attempts to transplant a liver from a corpse. All have been done at the University of Colorado, and all patients have died, although they have survived for periods ranging from six days to over three weeks.

At this point, spleen transplants seem completely unsuccessful, with the spleen not functioning at all following the operation.

Francis Moore of the Peter Bent Brigham Hospital has made certain refinements of the transplant technique which cut operating time by about 30 per cent and thus improve the odds for survival of the operation at least.

One of the world's experts on rejection of foreign tissue is the British immunologist, Peter B. Medawar, Nobel Prize winner and director of Britain's National Institute of Medical Research. Among the numerous pre-transplant tests he has devised to aid in selection of donors is one in which living lymphocytes from the blood of an intended recipient are injected between the layers of skin of the potential donor. The preferred donor has the least inflammation of the area.

At the Cleveland Clinic, they are using an artificial kidney outside the body to keep kidney failures alive until they can receive a transplant. It was Willem Kolff, now head of the Clinic's department of artificial organs, who made the first artificial kidney in the Netherlands during the Nazi occupation. He used the cellophane casing for sausages, a roll of window screen and a tank for his original "dialyzer," through which the impure blood circulates, is cleansed and returned to the patient. Today, many kidney patients have been kept alive for years through dialysis, supplemented by transfusions and drugs.

The most ambitious project now under way in the realm of surgery is the perfection of an artificial heart. The question today is no longer "if" but "when." Dr. C. Walton Lillehei, heart specialist at the University of Minnesota, predicts it will be ten years at least before such a thing is possible. Dr. DeBakey gives it three to five years, and Dr. Kolff, who implanted an artificial heart in a calf which lived twenty-nine hours after the operation, says if a synthetic heart has not replaced a human heart in three years, he will be disappointed.

Silicone rubber seems to have the best properties for such a heart. But still unanswered are the questions of how to power this greatest of all pumps, and how to adjust it to physical and emotional reactions.

Thirty years ago, even the most progressive surgeon would have considered these plans for an artificial heart—or even entering the heart at all—wild flights of the imagination straight out of science fiction.

But a courageous team at Johns Hopkins, one a pediatric cardiologist, Helen Brooke Taussig; the other, a vascular surgeon, Alfred Blalock, changed the course of heart surgery for all future generations. Their story is told in detail in the pages that follow.

HELEN TAUSSIG AND
ALFRED BLALOCK

Pioneer Team in the Evolution of
Children's Heart Surgery

[1898–   ]   [1899–1964]

HELEN TAUSSIG and Alfred Blalock of Johns Hopkins had
the rare privilege of seeing the immediate value of the operation they devised well over one thousand times while the patient was still on the operating table. But to Dr. Taussig the
first time she saw it is a memory she will always cherish.*

She had suggested the radically new heart operation. Dr.
Blalock was performing it. The patient was a pitifully small,
six-year-old boy, blue and dying from lack of oxygen in his
blood, and no longer able to walk. The surgeon had rerouted
his blood circulation, and removed the clamps when the blood
welled up in the child's chest. Dr. Blalock quickly controlled
the hemorrhage and poured in plasma.

Suddenly, a physician who was giving the anaesthetic cried,
"He's a lovely color now!" Dr. Taussig walked to the head
of the operating table and saw what she describes as "his
lovely, normal pink lips."

*Most of the material included in this chapter is based on an interview
the author had with Dr. Taussig in December, 1964, plus written material
she very generously made available to the author.

134

In a few minutes, the child awoke, still in the operating room, and asked, "Is the operation over?"

"Yes," answered Dr. Blalock.

"May I get up now?" And from that moment on the former patient was a normal, well and happy child.

The boy was the third life saved by this team whose "blue baby" operation is probably the most dramatic and well-known surgical feat in modern medical history. He was memorable to Dr. Taussig mainly because it was the first time life had so obviously returned under her immediate observation. And this was but the beginning of the life-saving operation for thousands of children throughout the world. The year was 1944.

The operation gave the green light to the then very new field of cardiac surgery. Open heart operations performed today would not have been considered without the impetus from the Taussig-Blalock innovations.

Dr. Taussig never planned to become a pediatric cardiologist; she seemed to be led into it, step by step. The brilliant daughter of Frank Taussig, who was professor of economics at Harvard for fifty years, Helen Brooke Taussig was born in 1898 in Cambridge, Massachusetts. She was refused admittance to Harvard Medical School because she was a woman. And although women were permitted to study at Harvard's School of Public Health, they were not admitted as candidates for degrees.

"That was the deciding factor which led me to study medicine," she says, providing a clue to the kind of person she is, thriving on challenges, a very feminine but practical St. George in a white coat, attacking illness, ignorance, complacency, prejudice, timidity and the other ills of mankind. But always with a twinkle in her eyes.

She considers such statements as "It can't be done," or "It has always been done this way" as a personal call to action. The results of her activist nature have left their mark in areas far removed from the "blue baby" operation, although it was through this that she achieved her original fame.

Because she could not get into Harvard, she studied anatomy at Boston University. There, in 1922, the dean of the medical school one day handed her a beef heart to study, saying it would do her "no harm to be interested in one of the larger organs of the body." Two years later, Helen Taussig was urged to transfer to Johns Hopkins to complete her medical training. As a medical student, she worked in Hopkins' heart station, under Dr. Edward Carter, who offered her a fellowship in his laboratory when the department of medicine refused her an internship upon her graduation.

In 1930, she was put in charge of the Children's Cardiac Clinic at Hopkins. At that time, the Clinic consisted of a social worker, a technician and an electrocardiograph machine. Soon thereafter, a fluoroscope was added. Dr. Edwards A. Park, the great pediatrician, chief of the pediatric department, had started the special clinics to study certain childhood diseases at Hopkins. He told her, "Now, Dr. Taussig, you are going to learn congenital malformations of the heart. And when you do," he added, "it will be a great day."

She had little enthusiasm for the assignment, but, in her thorough New England manner, set about to learn all she could concerning rheumatic fever—then one of the prime causes of children's heart trouble—and congenital malformations. The latter are defects present at birth.

Observations on two "blue babies" with apparent absence of the right ventricle convinced her that malformations of the heart repeated themselves and that similar malformations

136

caused similar changes in the size and shape of the heart. She was encouraged to find that her diagnosis for both babies had been substantiated by the electrocardiogram. When these babies died, the diagnosis was proven to be correct. At that point, she says, "the key to clinical diagnosis of malformations of the heart had been turned."

The "great day" was dawning.

Dr. Taussig began to realize that defects in the heart were depriving the lungs of blood, and blood must receive oxygen from passage through the lungs or the child becomes cyanotic (blue) and dies. Central to the problem was a ductus, or an abnormality in a passageway from the heart, that was closing and squeezing off the needed supply of blood to the lungs.

She tried to interest surgeons in creating a ductus that would work, but no one seemed to catch her enthusiasm. One of these was Dr. Robert Gross, a Boston surgeon, who in 1939 first succeeded in closing the opening between the aorta and the pulmonary artery in a child suffering from this cardiac defect known as a "patent ductus." So she bided her time until Alfred Blalock arrived at Johns Hopkins, in 1942, as surgeon-in-chief. He was a well-known vascular surgeon who had already performed several operations for a patent ductus, the exact opposite of the solution to the "blue baby" problem.

After his first patent ductus operation at Hopkins, Dr. Taussig complimented him on his surgical skill . . . but added that she was waiting for the day when he would *build* a ductus for a child dying of anoxemia (lack of oxygen in the blood) and "not when you tie off a ductus for a child with a little too much blood going to his lungs."

Dr. Blalock sighed and replied, "When that day comes, this will seem like child's play."

Two years later to the day, he did his first "blue baby" operation.

The intervening years were full of experiments on animals, performed in the Johns Hopkins laboratory by Dr. Blalock's talented surgical technician, Vivian Thomas.* It took a great deal of time to create cyanosis, in the first place, in order that they could experiment with an operation to correct it.

Also, in this time, Dr. Blalock was working on an operation to treat constriction of the aorta. He and several surgeons achieved success almost simultaneously, but with different approaches to the problem. Dr. Blalock's solution was to by-pass the trouble spot and connect the carotid artery to the descending aorta.

Dr. Taussig immediately saw the application of this surgical technique to save the cyanotic child. She suggested to Dr. Blalock that he could bypass the pulmonary stenosis, and put the subclavian artery into the pulmonary artery, thus re-routing the bloodstream for "blue babies." Dr. Blalock listened attentively.

After animal experiments showing that the idea would work, Dr. Blalock went ahead with the first such operation ever performed—with Dr. Taussig standing at his side in the operating room.

It was a success. Within the next five years, this team had performed some one thousand "blue baby" operations, with 78 per cent showing marked improvement and consequently prolonged life. Dr. Taussig diagnosed and Dr. Blalock operated, but the two worked together in complete harmony.

As a result of this teamwork, over five thousand heart

*The author has first-hand knowledge of Vivian Thomas' extraordinary competence in animal surgery. Thanks to his skill in repairing a diaphragmatic hernia in a cat, the author's beloved pet, "Little Doc" came with flying colors through an operation that only one out of four cats survive!

operations were performed on children before Dr. Blalock's death in September 1964. By now, thousands more have been performed throughout the world by surgeons trained under the two pioneers. It is impossible to count the lives that have been saved through this procedure, for it was not only "blue babies" who benefited, but countless others who have since undergone heart surgery that would never have been attempted without the impetus gained from the Taussig-Blalock innovation.

Did it take a great deal of courage to suggest the first operation to correct cyanosis? Dr. Taussig answered this question for me with her customary bemused composure. "It doesn't take much courage to decide to operate on a child dying from lack of oxygen," she said. "Not when you know the operation is the only chance he has to live."

After thirty-three years as physician-in-charge of the Cardiac Clinic of the Harriet Lane (children's) section of Johns Hopkins, Helen Brooke Taussig retired from that position at the age of sixty-five in 1963. But she has just begun to fight, for, a great humanitarian as well as a physician, she is currently sharpening her rapier to do battle against less specific foes than cyanosis, all in the interest of her fellow man.

She became President-elect of the American Heart Association, in 1964 and becomes President in October, 1965, the first woman president in its forty years of existence.

She is still in her office at Johns Hopkins, and it is still a kind of "heart shrine" to all those who know her. But most of her energy and youthful inquisitiveness is pouring into research on the causes of congenital malformations. It is good to be able to correct defects, she believes, but it is better to prevent them altogether. To aid in her research, she was awarded the Thomas M. Rivers memorial distinguished fellowship upon the occasion of her retirement in 1963. All of the forty thousand dollars will go toward enabling her to do research.

Currently hot on the trail of the variable effects of vitamin D on body chemistry, she is gleefully pursuing the culprit, although she knows—and takes in her stride the fact—that she is risking opposition to her findings from some drug manufacturers if those findings confirm her suspicions. She suspects that the reactions of some pregnant women to vitamin D may be a cause of the build-up of substances that injure the entire vascular system in their babies. And could it be that this same process contributes to hardening of the arteries of the aging, when substances also build up in the blood vessels? Could an individual's susceptibility to vitamin D be one of the factors responsible?

Helen Taussig won't stop until she gets the answer—just as she didn't stop until she had alerted pediatricians and then Congress to the dangers of thalidomide and its devastating damage to the limbs of unborn babies.

On a tip from a former student that "something horrible" was happening in Europe, causing children to be born deformed, Dr. Taussig took off for Germany to investigate for herself. All the evidence she gathered from physicians there pointed to thalidomide as the cause. She lost no time in reporting her findings immediately on her return to the United States to a meeting of the American Pediatric Society, even though she was not scheduled to speak. Congress was at that time involved in hearings concerning drugs and the drug industry, and Helen Taussig asked to appear before the committee.

"I broke all the rules," she says with obvious delight. She showed slides and gave her report, telling them everything she knew of the tragic consequences of what had seemed to be a harmless sleeping pill. And she refused to be intimidated.

"Are you a pharmacologist?" asked a committee member with some sarcasm.

"I may be no pharmacologist," she answered, "but I'm sure that any one of you who has a child or a grandchild would do the same thing that I am doing now, if you had seen what I have seen."

The hearings had been going badly and seemed destined to produce none of the legislation needed to control injudicious sales, labeling and use of untested drugs. It was Dr. Helen Taussig's testimony that turned the tide. Fortunately, Dr. Frances Kelsey of the Food and Drug Administration had also been awake to the dangers of thalidomide and had kept it off the American market. These two women deserve the credit not only for saving countless American babies from deformity, but also for being instrumental in the passage of a bill to protect the public from any such reckless drug practices.

Dr. Taussig has received many professional honors from her own government and foreign governments as well. But her greatest recognition came in September 1964, when President Johnson awarded her the highest civilian honor this country can bestow—the Medal of Freedom.

Her citation reads:

"Physician, physiologist and embryologist, her fundamental concepts have made possible the modern surgery of the heart which enables countless children to lead productive lives."

She is that and more, but Helen Taussig is the first to remind people that she was part of a team—Taussig and Blalock of Hopkins.

She actually received the award on September 14, the day before Dr. Blalock's death.

And what kind of a man was Dr. Blalock?

When he died, the Baltimore *Evening Sun* had this to say about him in an editorial: "The prestige of the Johns Hopkins has long been sufficient to attract men of the first rank. And this very circumstance, in perspective, will help attest to the status of Dr. Alfred Blalock—the fact that he stood out even in such a company."

Born in Georgia in 1899, he came to Johns Hopkins in 1918. Seven years later, he was graduated as a surgeon and went to the Vanderbilt University Hospital and School of Medicine, where he had become full professor before returning to Hopkins as surgeon-in-chief in 1942.

A gentle, quiet man, Dr. Blalock inspired confidence in all those he worked with or taught. He believed in people and he helped many to believe in themselves.

"There is nothing magical about science or scientific investigators," he said once. "The conception of the scientist as an intellectual superman achieving important results through sheer brilliance is quite unfounded. Too often, in talking to a bright young surgeon, I have heard the statement that he cannot make contributions to the advancement of surgery because he has no originality, when, as a matter of fact, he has not had the opportunity or the inspiration to demonstrate his ability. I am confident that many of us can make contributions if we are interested, if we observe carefully, and if we work hard."

Alfred Blalock worked hard all his life. Long before the "blue baby" operation brought him fame, he and his collaborators had published over one hundred scientific papers, primarily on the dynamics of normal and pathological cardiovascular systems. He established what has been called the

Blalock school of experimental surgery, which entails a comprehensive understanding of the physiology, biochemistry, and biophysics of damaged or malformed tissues.

But he always felt his most important contribution was the training of those who would teach others. He trained between fifty and fifty-five residents in surgery during his twenty-two years as surgeon-in-chief at Hopkins. About half of them are leading cardiovascular surgeons in the United States and in numerous foreign countries. At least a dozen are chairmen of departments of surgery at other hospitals. He left his mark on thousands more.

Although he had performed innumerable and extremely difficult cardiovascular operations before the "blue baby" one, he recognized its historical significance above all the others. He felt that its success had given surgeons the courage to attack problems of heart disorders, and it had ushered in the modern era of heart surgery.

Shortly after his retirement, and two months before his death from cancer, Dr. Blalock had the rare pleasure of being present when the Johns Hopkins Clinical Science Building was renamed in his honor.

Inscribed in marble in the foyer of the Blalock Building are these words:

"This marble from the Surgical Amphitheater on this site from 1904 to 1951 honors all who developed surgery at Johns Hopkins and in so doing exerted an influence which has extended far beyond this institution."

Few exerted such an influence as Alfred Blalock and Helen Taussig.

After the "blue baby" operation proved successful, the way to open heart surgery was clear. The two Hopkins physicians would be the first to admit that there were many who came before them who had paved the way, but none had really traveled it before in the bold way they did.

One of the heroes in the medical world is Dr. Werner Forssman, who passed a catheter, or tube, into his own heart and verified its position by fluoroscope, just to prove the safety and value of this diagnostic tool in heart cases. The experiment took place in Germany in 1929. He repeated the procedure as added proof. But when he applied for a grant to study the circulation, he was dismissed from the hospital for making such a radical proposal!

Twelve years later, another physician, André Cournand, heard of the experiment and recognized the worth of the catheter in the study of cardiopulmonary physiology. He and Dr. Dickenson Richards perfected the technique of cardiac catheterization. In 1956, Forssman, Cournand and Richards received the Nobel Prize for Medicine and Physiology.

Another diagnostic tool was the injection of a radio-opaque material into the right ventricle, to establish its position. This is called angio-cardiography.

But, despite the importance of these diagnostic techniques today, it is still noteworthy to recall that Dr. Blalock had done a hundred and fifty operations on children with decreased pulmonary blood flow before cardiac catheterization or angio-cardiography were available at Hopkins.

Up to 1953, although there were operations within the heart, they were done "blind," with the skilled surgeons working by touch alone. The heart was pumping gallons of blood around the body as the surgeons worked, and there seemed no way to stop it. Robert Gross devised techniques to isolate one part of the heart so that he could work without stopping the whole pump.

Then two radical inventions changed the picture. One was

hypothermia, or lowering the body's temperature, and allowing the heart to be cut off from circulation for a few minutes without damage. The other was extracorporeal circulation, in which a machine outside the body takes over for the heart and lungs during the operation. Both are discussed elsewhere in this book.

Today, hearts operate in active human beings with tiny electronic pacemakers to adjust the beat, rerouted blood passages, manmade valves, and patches. However, heart surgery is still in its infancy. The mortality rate still leaves room for improvement, and there are hopes that life expectancy can be raised following heart surgery.

But the greatest hope lies with prevention of cardiac abnormalities and disease. The most vocal spokesman for this hope is the President of the American Heart Association—Helen Taussig herself.

"Though some of my younger colleagues insist it will be impossible," she says, "I think perhaps there may come a day when man can alter the genetic forces that produce malformations. Altering genetics for the good of mankind may seem unthinkable now. We know so little about genetics. But after all, it does not seem altogether illogical to me to suppose that, once we find out what genetic forces produce abnormalities, we can then proceed to do something about them."

"WHAT'S PAST IS PROLOGUE"
The "Doers"

I<small>T</small> IS almost axiomatic that those who achieve immortality by having their names and deeds inscribed in history books, do so only after they themselves have passed into history. The men and women who grace the pages of this book share the unique distinction of having achieved immortality in their lifetimes.

From Eliot and Rusk to Cobb and Freud, this is a chronicle of the men and women whose innovations have radically changed the face of medicine within our lifetime and theirs. The innovators or "doers" represent almost all areas of the medical sciences, including anatomy, anthropology, bacteriology, biochemistry, cardiology, immunology, medicine, mental health, pediatrics, physical medicine, psychiatry (adult and child), public health and surgery (cardiac, children's, neuro, orthopedic and general). Within the various specialty areas, the doers fall into categories that run the gamut from individual researchers and practitioners to highly organized teams of researchers, group practitioners, and surgical teams covering the major subspecialties.

As to the contributions themselves, the roster reads like an instant history of twentieth-century medicine, to wit, the beginning of private group practice, the founding of the com-

146

munity mental health clinic movement, the development of the "third phase" of medicine, the conquest of polio, the development of spare parts, transplants, and the use of ultrasound and sonar in surgery, the "blue baby" breakthrough in cardiac surgery, the emergence of laser as a weapon against cancer. Underpinning all these specific innovations are the across-the-board revolutionary changes that were brought about in public health, child care, cardiology, psychiatric research and training, physical anthropology and child analysis and therapy by the other doers included in this volume.

The history of medicine, if written in terms of "deeds and doers," might sound much like the classic legends of Greek or English literature. The standard formula with the latter is always the same: the hero or gladiator or knight is a super kind of doer who performs a super kind of deed which instantaneously changes the status quo from black to white in the here and now and forever after! Medical history is not and cannot be written this way, however, because the historic breakthroughs in medicine do not fit the quick and easy, black and white, classic model. In medicine, the interim between cause and effect is often so long and the steps between them so complex that many medical historians have avoided tackling this kind of story altogether. Unfortunately, in many instances, this has led to leaving unwritten the events that take place in the interim between the time of a discovery and its use, as well as the complex process involved in its translation into community action. The story of polio is a case in point. The historian's job in documenting the long, painstaking building-block research, followed by animal trials, human trials and the whole process that finally wound up in a mass vaccination program was a formidable one! Fortunately, it was undertaken and, as a result, we now have a notion of what it takes in the way of time, effort, money, but, above all, *people other than the innovators* to get from the drawing board to the final launching of a full-scale program. The telling of this story is important, not because it happens to be a gem in the annals of medical history, but because it explains why many brilliant research ideas never get beyond the drawing board. In the long history of medicine, there is ample evidence to show that some of the research concepts being programmed today are identical with some in the past which, like the kingdom for want of a horse, for want of a shoe, for want of a nail were lost!

The "Facilitators"

Who are the facilitators? What do they have that other men seem to lack? What special qualities or strengths do they possess that make them able to catalyze, to bring into being and action other men's ideas, theories and trial experiments?

They are people who come from every walk of life and every profession. Some are lawyers, jurists, legislators; some are clergymen, educators, historians; some are writers, producers, journalists; some are community leaders. Among the latter are those who come from the ranks of industry, labor, civic organizations and politics. Finally, there are those who themselves are physicians and scientists, but who see their primary role as a facilitating one.

Examples from the distant past would include such names as Florence Nightingale, Dorothea Dix, Father Damien, Clifford Beers, Oliver Wendell Holmes. In the roster of those from the recent past up to and including the present would be names like Franklin D. Roosevelt (polio); Henry E. Sigerst (medical history); Abraham Flexner (medical education); Albert Schweitzer (medical missions); Stanley L. Kramer (producer of documentary films on the mentally ill and mentally retarded); Senator Lister Hill of Alabama and Representative John E. Fogarty of Rhode Island (health legislation).

Of those who have played a crucial, catalytic role in translating research into action, two names stand out above all the rest—Albert Deutsch and John Fitzgerald Kennedy. These two men, the one a crusading journalist, the other a brilliant and inspiring leader, lit candles in the darkest areas of human suffering—mental illness and mental retardation. As a result of the courageous crusading of Albert Deutsch and the persuasive prodding of John F. Kennedy, Congress, in 1963, enacted into law an historic piece of legislation, Public Law 88–164, called the "Mental Retardation Facilities and Community Mental Health Centers Construction Act of 1963." This law grew out of a series of recommendations made by the Joint Commission on Mental Illness and Health in its report called *Action for Mental Health* published in 1961. The report was based on the five-year study carried out by the Commission under a mandate provided by Congress when it enacted the Mental Health Study Act of 1955.

Only in America could two men with such striking differences in background, education and worldly goods show such startling resemblances to each other in things like personal attributes, characteristics and values and certain similar life experiences.

Albert Deutsch was born in the slum area of New York's lower East Side on October 23, 1905. He was the first child to be born in America of a family which had emigrated from Latvia in 1904.

The fourth of nine children, his childhood was spent in harsh poverty. At the age of five, while playing in the street with other children, his right eye was pierced by broken glass, necessitating removal of the eye. "This rarely mentioned experience, at so early an age, nevertheless had an inevitable effect on his development. In time, the surface of the wound healed, and the young child returned from a crowded city hospital to the warm family surroundings and grew in the rough and tumble of a large family. But there had already been born that divergent combination of inexorable, self-preserving independence in human relations joined with a deep sympathy for the adversities of others." *

Albert Deutsch's formal education ended with public high school. The rest of his education he got from hours spent in the New York Public Library and libraries all over the country after he finished high school and left home for good. He embarked on a career which began with years of wandering and odd jobs and ended with his being recognized as one of the leading medical and social welfare historians of this century. His best known books include *The Mentally Ill in America, One Hundred Years of American Psychiatry, The History of Public Welfare in New York State, The Shame of the States, Our Rejected Children* and *The Trouble with Cops.* For his work in the field of mental health, the American Psychiatric Association in 1958 awarded him its highest honor for a layman: election as an Honorary Fellow of the Association. At the time of his death in 1961, he was working on a book—a survey of mental health research in the United States.

John Fitzgerald Kennedy was born on May 29, 1917, in Brookline, Massachusetts, the son of Rose Fitzgerald and Joseph P. Kennedy. His father, who later became the United States ambassador to England and a multimillionaire, began life as a third-generation Irish-American in Boston.

John Kennedy first attended Princeton University and later graduated from Harvard University in 1940 where he received a

Jeanne L. Brand: "Albert Deutsch: The Historian as Social Reformer," Journal of the History of Medicine and Allied Sciences, Vol. XVIII, No. 2, 1963.

Bachelor of Science, *Cum laude*. He enlisted in the United States Navy in 1941, saw action and received decorations for performance as a PT Boat commander and was discharged in 1945. He was elected Representative from Massachusetts and served in the Congress from 1947–53. He was elected Senator from Massachusetts in 1952 and again in 1958. He was elected President of the United States in 1960. He served his country in that office from January 21, 1961, to the date of his death, November 22, 1963.

Kennedy was the author of several books, one of which, *Profiles in Courage*, won the Pulitzer Prize for biography in 1957. In 1963 he sent his now famous message to Congress requesting legislation in the area of mental health. In so doing, he became the first President of the United States to send a special message to that body in behalf of the mentally ill and the mentally retarded. This

This brings us back to the question raised earlier and left unanswered, namely, "What special qualities or strengths do they [the facilitators] possess that make them able to catalyze, to bring into being and action other men's ideas, theories and trial experiments?" The examples cited above should give a clue to the answer. They are all men of integrity, courage, vision, with a deep and abiding concern for their fellow men. But they are something more. They are men who have a unique ability to convert theory into tried and proven, to translate aspiration into action, to transform concept into concrete. They are men who in their passion for justice will forever "disturb the comfortable and comfort the disturbed." They are men committed to a quality of excellence which makes them unable to give less than their best but, in the interim, when choices must be weighed and decisions made, are able to "tolerate uncertainty with equanimity." Above all, as Eric Sevareid said of Edward R. Murrow, they are men with "magic in them that makes their presence a moment of magic."

These, then, are the facilitators, past and present, who,

together with the doers, have advanced modern medicine to its present state. To bring into being future advances already visible on the medical horizon will require new recruits in the ranks of each.

"Whereof what's past is prologue, what to come in yours and my discharge." *

*William Shakespeare. The Tempest, Act II, Scene 1.

INDEX

CAROLINE A. CHANDLER

a descendant of the Chandler family which settled in Roxbury in 1634, attended Mt. Aloysius Academy, Cresson, Pennsylvania, and from Barnard College went to Yale Medical School, where she won her first spurs in her chosen fields—medical research and pediatrics. She continued her research first at the Harvard Medical School and later at the Johns Hopkins School of Medicine.

During the war, Dr. Chandler left the laboratory to carry out a special project for the Children's Bureau in Washington and later was commissioned Surgeon (R) in the United States Public Health Service, an appointment she continues to hold.

She returned to Johns Hopkins after the war as Assistant Professor of Pediatrics, first on a full time basis—later, on a part time basis as her interest shifted more and more toward working with community groups and agencies serving the public. Thus, after serving for three years as medical director of the Family and Children's Society, an adoption and child care agency in Baltimore, she accepted an assignment with the Maryland State Department of Health as director of a combined program of mental health and child health.

In 1961, Dr. Chandler joined the staff of the National Institute of Mental Health as chief of the Demonstrations Section of the Community Services Branch. She now heads up the newly created Child Mental Health Section of the Community Research and Services Branch of the NIMH. In addition, she maintains her association with Johns Hopkins through her continuing appointment as Assistant Professor of Pediatrics and Instructor in Mental Hygiene.

This good author writes from her own rich and rewarding experience.